Teacher's Resource Masters
Number and Operations—Fractions

Daily Common Core Review

Reteaching

Practice

Enrichment

DISCARD

Scott Foresman·Addison Wesley

enVisionMATH®
Common Core

PEARSON

Glenview, Illinois • Boston, Massachusetts • Chandler, Arizona • Upper Saddle River, New Jersey

PEARSON

ISBN-13: 978-0-328-68793-0
ISBN-10: 0-328-68793-6

3 4 5 6 7 8 9 10 V011 15 14 13 12

Domain
Number and Operations—Fractions

Topic 11	**Fraction Equivalence and Ordering**
Topic 12	**Adding and Subtracting Fractions and Mixed Numbers with Like Denominators**
Topic 13	**Extending Fraction Concepts**

Each lesson has a Teacher Resource Master for Daily
Common Core Review, Reteaching, Practice and Enrichment.

Topic 11 **Fraction Equivalence and Ordering**

Daily Common Core Review (D), Reteaching (R),
Practice (P) and Enrichment (E) ....11-1 through 11-8

Topic 12 **Adding and Subtracting Fractions and Mixed Numbers with Like Denominators**

Daily Common Core Review (D), Reteaching (R),
Practice (P) and Enrichment (E) .... 12-1 through 12-11

Topic 13 **Extending Fraction Concepts**

Daily Common Core Review (D), Reteaching (R),
Practice (P) and Enrichment (E) .... 13-1 through 13-10

1. Juan has 216 beach balls. Each beach ball has 16 stripes. How many stripes are there in all?

   A 1,296

   B 2,160

   C 3,456

   D 4,512

2. Steve picked 72 apples at the orchard. He plans to give all the apples away to 8 friends. How many apples will each friend get?

   A 9

   B 8

   C 7

   D 6

3. **Mental Math** Mary is sharing stickers from her collection with 4 of her friends. How many stickers will each friend receive if Mary distributes a total of 36 stickers?

   A 40

   B 32

   C 12

   D 9

4. How many marbles are left if 8 friends equally share a package of 75 marbles?

   _____

5. Roberto has 5 books. The number of pages in each book are 113, 152, 109, 122, and 131. Order the number of pages from least to greatest.

   _____

6. There are 60 minutes in an hour. How many minutes are there in 3 hours?

   _____

Name _____

Factors

When multiplying two numbers, you know that both numbers are factors of the product.

Example 1

Find the factors of 24.

Factors   Product

$1 \times 24 = 24$
$2 \times 12 = 24$
$3 \times 8 = 24$
$4 \times 6 = 24$

Factors of 24:
1, 2, 3, 4, 6, 8, 12, and 24

Example 2

Find the factors of 16.

What two numbers multiply together to equal 16?

$1 \times 16 = 16$
$2 \times 8 = 16$
$4 \times 4 = 16$
$8 \times 2 = 16$
$16 \times 1 = 16$

Factors of 16: 1, 2, 4, 8, and 16

List all the factors of each number.

1. 18

2. 21

3. 11

4. 14

5. 23

6. 33

7. Number Sense Irene wants to list all of the factors for the number 42. She writes 2, 3, 6, 7, 14, 21, and 42. Is she correct? Explain.

Name _____

Factors

For **1** through **12**, find all the factors of each number.

1. 54

2. 17

3. 28

4. 31

_____

_____

5. 44

6. 47

7. 77

8. 71

_____

_____

9. 65

10. 23

11. 57

12. 24

_____

_____

13. Karl's mother buys 60 party favors to give out as gifts during Karl's birthday party. Which number of guests will NOT let her divide the party favors evenly among the guests?

A 12   **B** 15   **C** 20   **D** 25

14. Writing to Explain Mrs. Fisher has 91 watches on display at her store. She says she can arrange them into rows and columns without any watches left over. Mr. Fisher says that she can only make 1 row with all 91 watches. Who is right and why?

_____

_____

_____

Name _____

Division Amazement

1. Trace a path to the middle of the maze. You can pass
through only if the remainder is 2 when you divide.

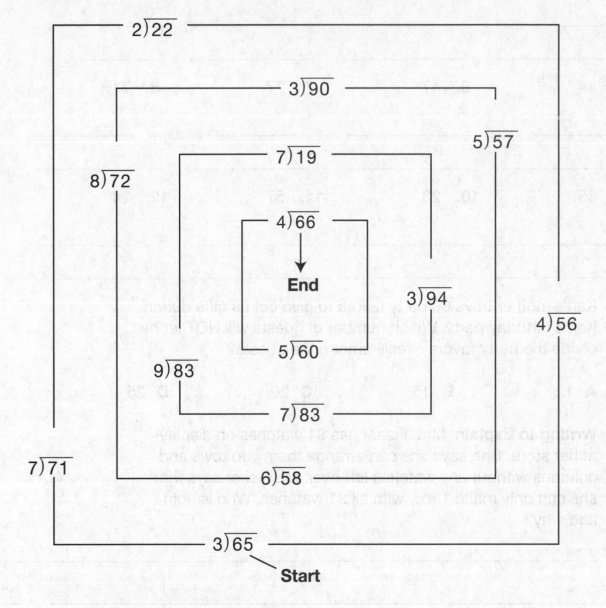

2. Solve **only** the problem described.   **a.** 2)91   **b.** 4)58   **c.** 8)79

- The quotient has 2 digits.

- The remainder is greater than 1.

1. Kevin is putting his baseball cards into an album. He has 450 cards and each page of the album holds 9 cards. How many pages will Kevin need if all 450 baseball cards are going in the album?

   A 50 pages

   B 40 pages

   C 25 pages

   D 5 pages

2. The population of Town A is 15,729. Town B has a population of 21,634. What is the total population of the two towns?

   A 35,372

   B 36,799

   C 37,255

   D 37,363

3. Wendy has 8 kinds of seashells in her collection. She has 122 of each kind of shell. How many seashells does she have in her collection?

   A 976

   B 866

   C 122

   D 8

4. **Estimation** The population of the city that Andrew lives in is 172,648. About how many people live in Andrew's city rounded to the nearest thousand?

   _____

5. Write all the ways you can express 24 as the product of 2 numbers.

   _____

   _____

   _____

6. Rita is making a necklace. She has 1 orange bead, 1 green bead, and 1 purple bead. How many possible ways can Rita arrange the beads?

   _____

7. Evaluate the expression for $x = 3$.

   $9 \times x + 1$

   _____

Prime and Composite Numbers

A **composite number** is a whole number greater than 1 that has more than two different factors. 15 has four different factors, 1, 3, 5, and 15, so 15 is a composite number.

A **prime number** is a whole number greater than 1 that has exactly two factors, itself and 1. 17 has exactly two factors, 1 and 17, so 17 is a prime number.

Example 1	**Example 2**
Is 7 a prime or composite number?	Is 6 a prime or composite number?
Find all the factors of 7.	Find all the factors of 6.
Factors of 7: 1, 7	Factors of 6: 1, 2, 3, 6
1 and 7 divide evenly into 7.	1, 2, 3, and 6 divide evenly into 6.
7 is a prime number because it only has two factors, the number itself and 1.	6 is a composite number because it has more than two factors.

Tell if the number is prime or composite.

1. 5

2. 12

3. 18

_____   _____   _____

4. 15

5. 37

6. 43

_____   _____   _____

Prime and
Composite Numbers

In **1** through **16**, write whether each number is prime or composite.

1. 81   **2.** 43   **3.** 572   **4.** 63

_____   _____   _____   _____

5. 53   **6.** 87   **7.** 3   **8.** 27

_____   _____   _____   _____

9. 88   **10.** 19   **11.** 69   **12.** 79

_____   _____   _____   _____

13. 3,235   **14.** 1,212   **15.** 57   **16.** 17

_____   _____   _____   _____

17. Mr. Gerry's class has 19 students, Ms. Vernon's class has 21 students, and Mr. Singh's class has 23 students. Whose class has a composite number of students?

_____

18. Every prime number greater than 10 has a digit in the ones place that is included in which set of numbers below?

    A 1, 3, 7, 9   **C** 0, 2, 4, 5, 6, 8

    B 1, 3, 5, 9   **D** 1, 3, 7

19. Writing to Explain Marla says that every number in the nineties is composite. Jackie says that one number in the nineties is prime. Who is correct? Explain your answer.

_____

_____

_____

Name _____

Pyramid Patterns

Suppose you are an ancient Egyptian stone worker. The queen has hired you to make a pyramid sculpture for her garden.

"I will give you 140 blocks of stone," she says. "Do not waste them."

The queen shows you a model using 14 blocks. The model is 3 layers high. The top layer has 1 block, the second layer has 4 blocks, and the third layer has 9 blocks.

A mathematician whispers to you, "You will be able to use all of the blocks if you follow the queen's model. Just look for the pattern."

After a while, the pattern becomes clear. You build the pyramid, using the blocks, and are richly rewarded by the queen.

1. How many layers does your finished pyramid have? _____

2. How many blocks did you use for each layer?

   _____

3. Describe the pattern the mathematician was talking about.

   _____

   _____

   _____

4. Could you make another pyramid with 200 blocks following the same pattern? Explain.

   _____

   _____

5. How many blocks of stone would you need to follow the same pattern and make a pyramid

   a. 8 layers high? _____   **b.** 9 layers high? _____

   c. 10 layers high? _____

Name _____

1. Which shape is split into 2 equal parts?

A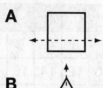

B

C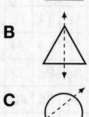

D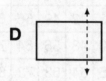

2. Shawn has a set of 125 marbles. He is organizing his marbles into 5 equal groups. How many marbles should he put in each group?

A 10

B 15

C 20

D 25

3. Mental Math Carla is 8 years old. Leo is 2 years younger than Carla. Katy is 6 years older than Leo. How old is Katy?

A 4

B 8

C 12

D 16

4. Maria says 1, 2, 3, 4, 6, and 12 are all of the factors of a number. What is the number?

_____

5. Mr. Thompson counted the total number of runners in the relay race. Each team had the same number of runners. Complete the pattern to find the number of runners counted. Then write the rule, and explain how you found the rule to complete the pattern.

4 8 12 16 _____ _____ _____

_____

_____

_____

_____

Multiples

You can use a multiplication table to help find some multiples for numbers.

What are some multiples of 5?

Step 1 Find the column for 5.

Step 2 All the numbers in that column are multiples of 5.

Tip You could use the row for 5 instead of the column for 5.

In the chart, the multiples of 5 are 5, 10, 15, 20, 25, 30, 35, 40, and 45.

×	1	2	3	4	5	6	7	8	9
1	1	2	3	4	⑤	6	7	8	9
2	2	4	6	8	10	12	14	16	18
3	3	6	9	12	15	18	21	24	27
4	4	8	12	16	20	24	28	32	36
5	5	10	15	20	25	30	35	40	45
6	6	12	18	24	30	36	42	48	54
7	7	14	21	28	35	42	49	56	63
8	8	16	24	32	40	48	56	64	72
9	9	18	27	36	45	54	63	72	81

In **1** through **8**, write five multiples of each number.

1. 3

2. 7

3. 9

4. 2

5. 1

6. 8

7. 6

8. 4

In **9** through **12**, tell whether the first number is a multiple of the second number.

9. 18, 3

10. 24, 6

11. 32, 7

12. 12, 4

13. Number Sense What number has 12, 24, and 30 as multiples? Explain how you found your answer.

Multiples

In **1** through **8**, write five multiples of each number.

1. 5   **2.** 3   **3.** 7   **4.** 4

_____   _____   _____   _____

5. 9   **6.** 2   **7.** 6   **8.** 8

_____   _____   _____   _____

In **9** through **16**, tell whether the first number is a multiple of the second number.

9. 21, 7   **10.** 28, 3   **11.** 17, 3   **12.** 20, 4

_____   _____   _____   _____

13. 54, 9   **14.** 15, 5   **15.** 26, 4   **16.** 32, 8

_____   _____   _____   _____

17. Circle the number in the box that is a multiple of 8.

10	18	20	24	31	36

18. Number Sense List five multiples for 3 and five multiples for 4. Then circle the common multiples.

_____

_____

19. Reasoning What number has factors of 2 and 3 and multiples of 12 and 18?

_____

20. What are five multiples of 9?

     A 9, 19, 29, 39, 49   **B** 9, 18, 27, 36, 45   **C** 1, 3, 9, 18, 27   **D** 1, 9, 18, 27, 36

21. Carmen listed the multiples of 6 as 1, 2, 3, and 6. Is she correct? Explain why or why not.

_____

_____

Name _____

Multiples or Factors?

Look at the numbers in each box.
Circle if they are multiples or factors, and write the number.

1. Factors

         of _____

Multiples

```
6     2
  3     1
```

2. Factors

         of _____

Multiples

```
16    40
   24    56
```

3. Factors

         of _____

Multiples

```
15    25
   40
```

4. Factors

         of _____

Multiples

```
2
    4
  1
```

Read the label for each box.
Write at least three numbers in each box that match the description.

5. Multiples of 3

6. Factors of 9

7. Factors of 8

8. Multiples of 7

1. Which of these is the number 200,601 in word form?

   A Two hundred thousand, six hundred one

   B Two hundred six thousand, one

   C Twenty thousand, six hundred one

   D Two thousand, six hundred one

2. Isabel walked 1,357 steps to get to school. Harold walked 935 steps to get to school. How many more steps did Isabel walk?

   A 492

   B 422

   C 392

   D 122

3. **Mental Math** Carl cut a 30-foot rope into 6-foot sections. How many 6-foot sections will Carl have?

   A 5

   B 4

   C 3

   D 2

4. Pedro has started a car-washing business. He charges $5 for each car he washes. On Saturday, Pedro washed 4 cars. On Sunday, he washed 7 cars. How much money did Pedro earn all together?

   _____

5. Zak takes 3 steps for every 2 steps Rich takes. How many steps will Zak take if Rich takes 18 steps? Explain how you found the answer. Make a table to help.

   _____

   _____

   _____

   _____

Name _____

Equivalent Fractions

If two fractions name the same amount, they are called **equivalent fractions**.

Use multiplication to write a fraction equivalent to $\frac{1}{2}$.

Multiply the numerator and denominator by the same number.

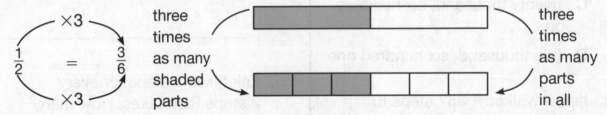

three times as many shaded parts

three times as many parts in all

$\frac{1}{2}$ and $\frac{3}{6}$ are equivalent fractions.

Use division to write a fraction that is equivalent to $\frac{10}{12}$.

Think of a number that is a factor of both 10 and 12. Two is a factor of 10 and 12. Divide the numerator and the denominator by 2.

$$\frac{10}{12} \xrightarrow{\div 2} \frac{5}{6}$$

$\frac{10}{12}$ and $\frac{5}{6}$ are equivalent fractions.

Find the missing number.

1. $\frac{1}{4} = \frac{\square}{8}$ ____

2. $\frac{9}{12} = \frac{\square}{4}$ ____

3. $\frac{2}{3} = \frac{\square}{6}$ ____

4. $\frac{4}{5} = \frac{\square}{10}$ ____

Multiply to find an equivalent fraction.

5. $\frac{1}{4} =$ ____

6. $\frac{1}{2} =$ ____

7. $\frac{1}{6} =$ ____

8. $\frac{3}{4} =$ ____

Divide to find an equivalent fraction.

9. $\frac{8}{12} =$ ____

10. $\frac{9}{12} =$ ____

11. $\frac{4}{8} =$ ____

12. $\frac{2}{6} =$ ____

13. $\frac{4}{10} =$ ____

14. $\frac{5}{10} =$ ____

15. $\frac{8}{10} =$ ____

16. $\frac{6}{8} =$ ____

Equivalent Fractions

Find the missing number.

1. $\frac{1}{2} = \frac{\square}{12}$

2. $\frac{6}{10} = \frac{\square}{5}$

3. $\frac{3}{12} = \frac{\square}{4}$

4. $\frac{4}{5} = \frac{\square}{10}$

_____   _____   _____   _____

Find an equivalent fraction.

5. $\frac{1}{2}$

6. $\frac{2}{12}$

7. $\frac{6}{10}$

8. $\frac{6}{8}$

9. $\frac{8}{12}$

_____   _____   _____   _____   _____

10. Is $\frac{2}{14}$ equivalent to $\frac{3}{7}$? _____

11. In Mark's collection of antique bottles, $\frac{1}{2}$ of the bottles
    are dark green. Write three equivalent fractions for $\frac{1}{2}$.

    _____

12. Write a pair of equivalent fractions for the picture below.

    _____

13. At the air show, $\frac{1}{3}$ of the airplanes were gliders.
    Which fraction is an equivalent fraction for $\frac{1}{3}$?

    A $\frac{4}{6}$ **B** $\frac{2}{12}$ **C** $\frac{4}{12}$ **D** $\frac{3}{6}$

14. In Missy's sports-card collection, $\frac{3}{4}$ of the cards are baseball
    cards. In Frank's collection, $\frac{8}{12}$ are baseball cards. Frank says
    they have the same fraction of baseball cards. Is he correct?

    _____

    _____

Playing the Part

1. You have 6 tiles. Of the tiles, $\frac{2}{6}$ are rectangles. The rest of the tiles are triangles. Draw a design using the tiles.

2. You have 10 tiles. Of the tiles, $\frac{4}{10}$ are rectangles. The rest of the tiles are triangles. Draw a design using the tiles.

3. You have 10 triangular tiles. Use $\frac{8}{10}$ of them to draw a design.

Students in Jeremy's class are working on 20 projects for the Science Fair. Use this information for **4** and **5**.

4. Four of the projects are about plants. What fraction of the projects are about plants?

5. Five of the projects are about animals. What fraction of the projects are about animals?

_____

_____

Use the table at the right for **6** through **8**.

6. What fraction of the train cars are tankers?

Train Cars	
Number	**Cars**
7	Flatcar
1	Engine
7	Tanker
9	Boxcar

_____

7. What fraction of the train cars are boxcars? Name an equivalent fraction for the fraction.

8. What fraction would represent all the cars in the train?

_____

_____

1. Gina buys $\frac{1}{4}$ of a yard of material to make a pillow. Which fraction is equivalent to $\frac{1}{4}$?

A $\frac{4}{8}$

B $\frac{3}{8}$

C $\frac{2}{8}$

D $\frac{1}{8}$

2. What fraction of these balls have stripes?

A $\frac{1}{4}$

B $\frac{1}{3}$

C $\frac{1}{2}$

D $\frac{3}{4}$

3. How many sides does a quadrilateral have?

_____

4. Let N be a whole number that is less than 100,000. Also, N has a 3 in the tens place and a 5 in the thousands place. What is the *greatest* possible value of N?

_____

5. Estimation Round 5,708 to the nearest ten.

_____

Number Lines and Equivalent Fractions

Write two equivalent fractions that name the point on the number line.

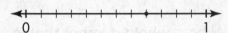

Step 1 Count the number of tick marks from 0 to 1.	**Step 2** Count the number of tick marks from 0 to where the point is.	**Step 3** 12 is an even number, so it can be divided by 2.
On this number line, there are 12. That tells you the denominator of one fraction is 12.	There are 8. That tells you the numerator of the fraction is 8. You now know one fraction that names the point is $\frac{8}{12}$.	$12 \div 2 = 6$

Step 3 (continued)

If you count every second tick mark from 0 to 1, you will count 6 tick marks. The denominator of another fraction is 6.

Now, count every second tick mark from 0 to the location of the point. There are 4, so the numerator of the fraction is 4. An equivalent fraction to $\frac{8}{12}$ is $\frac{4}{6}$.

$$\frac{8}{12} = \frac{4}{6}$$

Write two fractions that name the point on the number line.

1.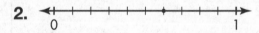

    _____

2.

    _____

3. **Draw a Diagram** Are $\frac{3}{8}$ and $\frac{3}{4}$ equivalent fractions? Draw a number line to show your answer.

    _____

    _____

    _____

Number Lines and Equivalent Fractions

Write two fractions that name each point on the number line.

1.

_____

2.

_____

3.

_____

4.

_____

5. Draw a number line to show that $\frac{2}{3}$ and $\frac{4}{6}$ are equivalent.

6. Draw a number line to show that $\frac{3}{5}$ and $\frac{6}{10}$ are equivalent.

7. Which of the following pairs are **NOT** equivalent fractions?

   A $\frac{1}{3}, \frac{5}{8}$ **B** $\frac{2}{4}, \frac{4}{8}$ **C** $\frac{3}{5}, \frac{6}{10}$ **D** $\frac{3}{4}, \frac{9}{12}$

8. **Writing to Explain** How many fractions are equivalent to $\frac{4}{5}$? Explain.

_____

_____

_____

Fraction Playground

To balance a seesaw at the playground, the two people on the seesaw must be the same weight. The same is true for fractions. Two equal fractions will result in a balanced seesaw. When one fraction on a seesaw is greater than the other fraction on the seesaw, the greater fraction will sink and the lesser fraction will rise.

Look at the fractions on the seesaws. For each, circle the fraction or fractions that would result in the seesaw staying in the position shown.

1.

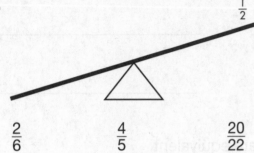

$\dfrac{2}{6}$ $\qquad$ $\dfrac{4}{5}$ $\qquad$ $\dfrac{20}{22}$ $\qquad$ $\dfrac{5}{6}$ $\qquad$ $\dfrac{1}{5}$

2.

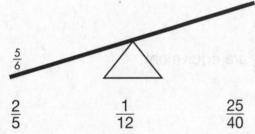

$\dfrac{2}{5}$ $\qquad$ $\dfrac{1}{12}$ $\qquad$ $\dfrac{25}{40}$ $\qquad$ $\dfrac{10}{20}$ $\qquad$ $\dfrac{8}{9}$

3. $\dfrac{4}{9}$

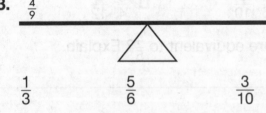

$\dfrac{1}{3}$ $\qquad$ $\dfrac{5}{6}$ $\qquad$ $\dfrac{3}{10}$ $\qquad$ $\dfrac{12}{25}$ $\qquad$ $\dfrac{20}{45}$

4. $\dfrac{2}{3}$

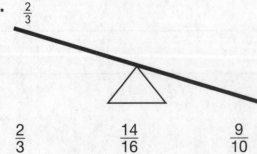

$\dfrac{2}{3}$ $\qquad$ $\dfrac{14}{16}$ $\qquad$ $\dfrac{9}{10}$ $\qquad$ $\dfrac{6}{18}$ $\qquad$ $\dfrac{12}{27}$

Name _____

1. Look at the model.

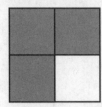

Which fraction is shown by
the model?

A $\frac{1}{4}$

B $\frac{1}{3}$

C $\frac{2}{3}$

D $\frac{3}{4}$

2. Janelle and Howard combined
all their pennies. Janelle had
213 pennies, and Howard had
468 pennies. How many pennies
did they have in all?

A 781

B 681

C 671

D 255

3. Where would placing the number 3
make the number sentence true?

A $15 \div 5 = \square$

B $42 \div \square = 7$

C $\square \div 5 = 9$

D $27 \div \square = 3$

4. Estimation Estimate the product
9×231. Show your work.

_____

_____

5. The numbers 25, 30, 35, 40 are all
multiples of what number?

_____

6. Marsha's school has 345 students.
If all the students are separated
into 5 equal groups, how many are
in each group?

_____

Comparing Fractions

Leanne wanted to compare $\frac{4}{6}$ and $\frac{3}{4}$. She used fraction strips to help.

				$\frac{1}{6}$	$\frac{1}{6}$	$\frac{4}{6}$
					$\frac{1}{4}$	$\frac{3}{4}$

She compared the amounts that were shaded in each picture. Because the amount shaded in $\frac{3}{4}$ is more than the amount shaded in $\frac{4}{6}$, she knew that $\frac{3}{4}$ is greater than $\frac{4}{6}$.

So, $\frac{3}{4} > \frac{4}{6}$.

Write $>$ or $<$ for each $\bigcirc$. Use fraction strips or benchmark fractions to help.

1. $\frac{5}{6} \bigcirc \frac{2}{3}$ **2.** $\frac{1}{5} \bigcirc \frac{2}{8}$ **3.** $\frac{9}{10} \bigcirc \frac{6}{8}$ **4.** $\frac{3}{4} \bigcirc \frac{1}{4}$

5. $\frac{7}{8} \bigcirc \frac{5}{10}$ **6.** $\frac{2}{5} \bigcirc \frac{2}{6}$ **7.** $\frac{1}{3} \bigcirc \frac{3}{8}$ **8.** $\frac{2}{10} \bigcirc \frac{3}{5}$

The same number of students attended school all week.

Day	Fraction of students buying lunch
Monday	$\frac{1}{2}$
Tuesday	$\frac{2}{5}$
Wednesday	$\frac{3}{4}$
Thursday	$\frac{5}{8}$
Friday	$\frac{4}{6}$

9. Did more students buy lunch on Tuesday or on Wednesday?   _____

10. Did more students buy lunch on Thursday or on Friday?   _____

Name _____

Comparing Fractions

Write > or < for each ◯. You may use fraction strips to help.

1. $\frac{1}{2}$ ◯ $\frac{3}{10}$ 2. $\frac{8}{12}$ ◯ $\frac{5}{12}$ 3. $\frac{3}{8}$ ◯ $\frac{1}{2}$

4. $\frac{3}{3}$ ◯ $\frac{7}{8}$ 5. $\frac{3}{5}$ ◯ $\frac{1}{3}$ 6. $\frac{1}{4}$ ◯ $\frac{2}{4}$

7. $\frac{5}{6}$ ◯ $\frac{5}{8}$ 8. $\frac{7}{12}$ ◯ $\frac{4}{5}$ 9. $\frac{3}{10}$ ◯ $\frac{6}{10}$

10. **Number Sense** Explain how you know that $\frac{21}{30}$ is greater than $\frac{2}{3}$.

_____

_____

_____

11. Tina completed $\frac{2}{3}$ of her homework.
George completed $\frac{7}{8}$ of his homework.
Who completed a greater fraction of homework? _____

12. Jackson played a video game for $\frac{1}{6}$ hour. Hailey played
a video game for $\frac{1}{3}$ hour. Who played the video game
for a greater amount of time? _____

13. Which fraction is greater than $\frac{3}{4}$?

A $\frac{1}{2}$ B $\frac{2}{5}$ C $\frac{5}{8}$ D $\frac{7}{8}$

14. **Writing to Explain** James says that $\frac{5}{5}$ is greater than $\frac{9}{10}$.
Is he correct? Explain.

_____

_____

_____

Comparing Outcomes

Tiffany tossed a number cube 12 times. Then she made a tally chart to show each time the cube showed each face.

Face	1	2	3	4	5	6
Number	I	III	II		II	IIII

1. Complete the table to show the fraction of tosses for each face of the number cube.

Face	1	2	3	4	5	6
Fraction (out of 12 tosses)	$\frac{1}{12}$					

Compare the fractional results for each face by writing >, <, or = in each ◯.

2. Face 1 ◯ Face 2

3. Face 3 ◯ Face 5

4. Face 5 ◯ Face 4

5. Face 2 ◯ Face 6

Tiffany tossed a coin 10 times and had 6 heads and 4 tails. Then she tossed a coin 20 times and had 8 heads and 12 tails.

6. Complete the table to show the fractions of heads and tails Tiffany tossed.

Outcome	Heads	Tails
Fraction out of 10		
Fraction out of 20		

Compare the fractional results for each set of tosses by writing >, <, or = in each ◯.

7. heads out of 10 ◯ tails out of 10

8. heads out of 20 ◯ tails out of 20

9. heads out of 10 ◯ heads out of 20

10. heads out of 10 ◯ tails out of 20

1. Which digit is in the thousands place in the number 661,239?

   A 9

   B 6

   C 3

   D 1

2. The two trays of pizza below show the amount of pizza left after the fourth-grade party.

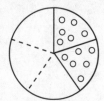

   Pepperoni   Mushroom

Which of the following compares the amount of pepperoni pizza left over to the amount of mushroom pizza left over?

   A $\frac{2}{5} > \frac{4}{10}$

   B $\frac{2}{10} < \frac{4}{5}$

   C $\frac{2}{5} = \frac{4}{10}$

   D $\frac{4}{10} > \frac{2}{5}$

3. The model is shaded to represent a fraction.

Which fraction below shows the fraction represented by the model in simplest form?

   A $\frac{1}{3}$

   B $\frac{1}{4}$

   C $\frac{1}{10}$

   D $\frac{1}{12}$

4. Complete the fact family below.

$$6 \times \underline{\hspace{1cm}} = 48$$

$$\underline{\hspace{1cm}} \times 6 = 48$$

$$\underline{\hspace{1cm}} \div 6 = 8$$

$$48 \div \underline{\hspace{1cm}} = 8$$

Tell what information is not needed. Then, solve the problem.

5. A farmer sells 12 dozen eggs to the market. She sells each dozen for $1. How many eggs does she sell to the market?

_____

_____

_____

_____

_____

6. In January of 2007, Mr. Edwards turned 64 years old. In what year was Mr. Edwards born?

_____

Ordering Fractions

How can you order fractions?

Order $\frac{2}{3}$, $\frac{1}{6}$, $\frac{7}{12}$ from least to greatest.

$\frac{1}{3}$			$\frac{1}{3}$			$\frac{1}{3}$		
$\frac{1}{6}$		$\frac{1}{6}$		$\frac{1}{6}$		$\frac{1}{6}$		$\frac{1}{6}$
$\frac{1}{12}$	$\frac{1}{12}$	$\frac{1}{12}$	$\frac{1}{12}$	$\frac{1}{12}$	$\frac{1}{12}$	$\frac{1}{12}$	$\frac{1}{12}$	$\frac{1}{12}$

Find equivalent fractions with a common denominator.

| $\frac{1}{12}$ | $\frac{1}{12}$ | $\frac{1}{12}$ | $\frac{1}{12}$ | $\frac{1}{12}$ | $\frac{1}{12}$ | $\frac{1}{12}$ | $\frac{1}{12}$ |

| $\frac{1}{12}$ | $\frac{1}{12}$ |

| $\frac{1}{12}$ | $\frac{1}{12}$ | $\frac{1}{12}$ | $\frac{1}{12}$ | $\frac{1}{12}$ | $\frac{1}{12}$ | $\frac{1}{12}$ |

Compare the numerators.
Order the fractions from least to greatest.
$\frac{2}{12} < \frac{7}{12} < \frac{8}{12}$.

Order the fractions from least to greatest.

1. $\frac{3}{10}$, $\frac{3}{6}$, $\frac{2}{5}$

$\frac{1}{10}$	$\frac{1}{10}$	$\frac{1}{10}$
$\frac{1}{5}$		$\frac{1}{5}$
$\frac{1}{6}$	$\frac{1}{6}$	$\frac{1}{6}$

2. $\frac{3}{8}$, $\frac{1}{3}$, $\frac{3}{12}$

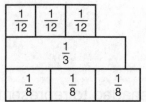

Find equivalent fractions with a common denominator and order from least to greatest.

3. $\frac{1}{2}$, $\frac{3}{4}$, $\frac{4}{6}$ _____

4. $\frac{3}{4}$, $\frac{2}{3}$, $\frac{7}{8}$ _____

5. $\frac{3}{10}$, $\frac{1}{2}$, $\frac{4}{5}$ _____

6. $\frac{1}{2}$, $\frac{3}{10}$, $\frac{3}{5}$ _____

7. $\frac{2}{3}$, $\frac{5}{6}$, $\frac{1}{2}$ _____

8. $\frac{5}{8}$, $\frac{3}{4}$, $\frac{3}{8}$ _____

Ordering Fractions

Order the fractions from least to greatest.

1. $\frac{3}{5}, \frac{7}{8}, \frac{5}{6}$

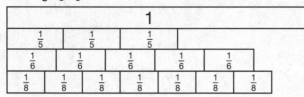

2. $\frac{1}{2}, \frac{7}{12}, \frac{4}{10}$

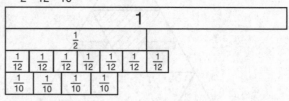

3. $\frac{2}{6}, \frac{1}{4}, \frac{5}{12}$

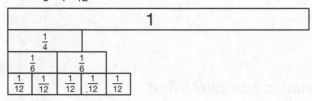

4. $\frac{3}{10}, \frac{2}{5}, \frac{1}{3}$

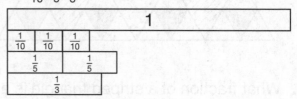

Find equivalent fractions with a common denominator and order from least to greatest.

5. $\frac{2}{3}, \frac{1}{2}, \frac{5}{12}$ _____

6. $\frac{1}{6}, \frac{1}{3}, \frac{3}{4}$ _____

7. $\frac{5}{6}, \frac{2}{3}, \frac{3}{4}$ _____

8. $\frac{7}{12}, \frac{2}{6}, \frac{1}{4}$ _____

9. $\frac{4}{5}, \frac{3}{10}, \frac{1}{2}$ _____

10. $\frac{9}{12}, \frac{1}{3}, \frac{3}{6}$ _____

11. Which fraction is greater than $\frac{2}{3}$?

A $\frac{1}{12}$ **B** $\frac{2}{6}$ **C** $\frac{5}{12}$ **D** $\frac{6}{8}$

12. Writing to Explain Explain how you know that $\frac{7}{12}$ is greater than $\frac{1}{3}$ but less than $\frac{2}{3}$?

_____

_____

_____

_____

Triangle Fractions

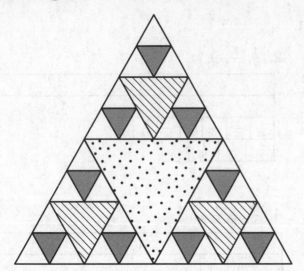

1. What fraction of a striped triangle is a shaded triangle? What
    fraction of the spotted triangle is a shaded triangle? Use >,
    <, or = to compare the two fractions.

    _____

2. What fraction of the spotted triangle is a white triangle? What
    fraction of a striped triangle is three shaded triangles? Use
    >, <, or = to compare the two fractions.

    _____

3. What fraction of the spotted triangle is two striped triangles?
    What fraction of the largest triangle is one spotted triangle?
    Use >, <, or = to compare the two fractions.

    _____

4. What fraction of the largest triangle is one striped triangle?
    What fraction of the largest triangle is four shaded triangles?
    Use >, <, or = to compare the two fractions.

    _____

Name _____

1. Where would placing the number 13 make the number sentence true?

A $4 \times 3 = \square$

B $5 \times \square = 115$

C $\square \times 12 = 168$

D $15 \times \square = 195$

2. What number on the number line does point *H* best represent?

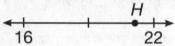

A 18

B 19

C 21

D 22

3. There are 63 students in the school band. At a band concert, Jerome saw that equal numbers of band members were seated in 3 different sections. How many band members were seated in each section?

A 21

B 14

C 7

D 3

4. Look at the model.

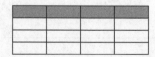

Which fraction is shown by the shaded part of the model?

A $\frac{1}{8}$ **C** $\frac{1}{4}$

B $\frac{1}{6}$ **D** $\frac{1}{2}$

5. What fraction of the triangles are shaded?

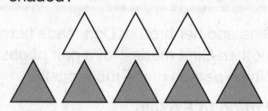

_____

6. Compare.

$\frac{5}{6}$ ◯ $\frac{7}{8}$

7. **Estimation** Look at the chart below. About what fraction of the goal have the fund-raisers reached?

$100	$200	$300	$400	$500

_____

_____

_____

_____

8. **Estimation** Round 1,249 to the nearest hundred.

_____

Problem Solving: Writing to Explain

Gina and her brother Don made homemade pasta with their mother. Gina made $\frac{1}{4}$ of a pan of pasta. Don made $\frac{3}{8}$ of a pan. Which person made more pasta?

Writing to Explain

- Write your explanation in steps to make it clear.

- Tell what the numbers mean in your explanation.

- Tell why you took certain steps.

Example

- Because $\frac{1}{4}$ and $\frac{3}{8}$ have different denominators, I multiplied the numerator and denominator of $\frac{1}{4}$ by 2 to get $\frac{2}{8}$.

- Then I could compare the numerators of $\frac{2}{8}$ and $\frac{3}{8}$. Because $\frac{3}{8}$ is greater than $\frac{2}{8}$ I knew that Don made more pasta.

1. Rick has a collection of 6 video games. He lets his best friend borrow $\frac{2}{6}$ of his video game collection. Write two fractions equivalent to this number. Explain how you came up with the fractions.

_____

_____

_____

_____

_____

_____

Problem Solving: Writing to Explain

1. Mary has 12 marbles. $\frac{3}{12}$ of the marbles are yellow and $\frac{2}{12}$ of the marbles are blue. The rest of the marbles are green. How many marbles are green? Explain how you know.

_____

_____

_____

_____

2. Adam wants to compare the fractions $\frac{3}{12}$, $\frac{1}{6}$, and $\frac{1}{3}$. He wants to order them from least to greatest and rewrite them so they all have the same denominator. Explain how Adam can rewrite the fractions.

_____

_____

_____

_____

3. Adam used the three fractions to make a circle graph and colored each a different color. What fraction of the graph is not colored? Explain your answer.

_____

_____

_____

Name _____

Shape Fractions

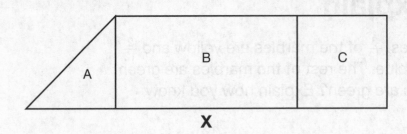

X

1. What fraction of trapezoid X is square C? Explain your answer.

_____

_____

2. What fraction of trapezoid X is rectangle B? Explain your answer.

_____

_____

3. What fraction of trapezoid X is triangle A? Explain your answer.

_____

_____

4. What fraction of shape Z is square J?
Explain your answer.

_____

_____

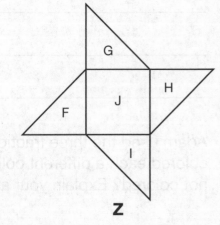

Z

5. What fraction of shape Z is triangle G? Explain.

_____

_____

1. Airport security guards choose some travelers for an extra safety check. So far, the guards have chosen the 6th, 12th, 18th, and 24th travelers in line. Which of these people will most likely be chosen for the extra safety check?

   A The 25th traveler in line

   B The 26th traveler in line

   C The 30th traveler in line

   D The 34th traveler in line

2. Shannon says, "My apartment number is a prime number." Which could be Shannon's apartment number?

   A 15

   B 27

   C 31

   D 44

3. Which fraction is equivalent to $\frac{3}{4}$?

   A $\frac{2}{6}$

   B $\frac{4}{8}$

   C $\frac{9}{12}$

   D $\frac{10}{12}$

4. Amin has $20. After buying 4 cans of tennis balls, he gets $8 back as change. How much did one can of tennis balls cost?

   _____

5. What are the next two numbers in this pattern? Describe the pattern.

   $\frac{12}{12}$ $\frac{10}{12}$ $\frac{8}{12}$ $\frac{6}{12}$ ___ ___

   _____

   _____

   _____

   _____

   _____

   _____

Modeling Addition of Fractions

Eight friends want to see a movie. Four of them want to see a comedy. Two want to see an action movie and two want to see a science-fiction movie. What fraction of the group wants to see either a comedy or a science-fiction movie?

You can use a model to add fractions.

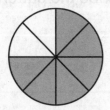

Look at the circle. It is divided into eighths, because there are eight people in the group. Each person represents $\frac{1}{8}$ of the group. Four people want to see a comedy. Shade in four of the sections to represent $\frac{4}{8}$. Two people want to see a science-fiction movie. Shade in two more sections to represent $\frac{2}{8}$. Count the number of shaded sections. There are six. So, $\frac{6}{8}$ of the group wants to see either a comedy or a science fiction movie.

$\frac{4}{8} + \frac{2}{8} = \frac{6}{8}$ Write the sum in simplest form. $\frac{6 \div 2}{8 \div 2} = \frac{3}{4}$

Find each sum. Simplify, if possible.

1. $\frac{2}{5} + \frac{1}{5}$ _____

2. $\frac{4}{6} + \frac{1}{6}$ _____

3. $\frac{3}{8} + \frac{3}{8}$ _____

4. $\frac{1}{6} + \frac{1}{6}$ _____

5. $\frac{2}{5} + \frac{3}{5}$ _____

6. $\frac{2}{10} + \frac{3}{10}$ _____

7. $\frac{5}{8} + \frac{3}{8}$ _____

8. $\frac{3}{10} + \frac{1}{10}$ _____

9. $\frac{3}{4} + \frac{1}{4}$ _____

10. $\frac{5}{10} + \frac{4}{10}$ _____

11. $\frac{1}{6} + \frac{1}{6} + \frac{1}{6}$ _____

12. $\frac{1}{12} + \frac{5}{12} + \frac{2}{12}$ _____

13. Number Sense We can express time as a fraction of an hour. For example, 15 minutes is $\frac{1}{4}$ hour. 30 minutes is $\frac{1}{2}$ hour. What fraction of an hour is 45 minutes? _____

Name _____

Modeling Addition
of Fractions

Find each sum. Simplify if possible. You may use fraction strips.

1. $\frac{1}{4} + \frac{1}{4}$ _____

2. $\frac{2}{5} + \frac{1}{5}$ _____

3. $\frac{3}{12} + \frac{1}{12}$ _____

4. $\frac{2}{6} + \frac{3}{6}$ _____

5. $\frac{1}{2} + \frac{2}{2}$ _____

6. $\frac{2}{8} + \frac{5}{8}$ _____

7. $\frac{3}{8} + \frac{3}{8}$ _____

8. $\frac{3}{10} + \frac{2}{10}$ _____

9. $\frac{1}{6} + \frac{2}{6}$ _____

10. **Draw a Picture** A rectangular garden is divided into 10 equal parts. Draw a picture that shows $\frac{3}{10} + \frac{3}{10} = \frac{6}{10}$, or $\frac{3}{5}$.

11. Each day, Steven walked $\frac{1}{12}$ mile more than the previous day. The first day he walked $\frac{1}{12}$, the second day he walked $\frac{2}{12}$ mile, the third day he walked $\frac{3}{12}$ mile. On which day did the sum of his walks total at least 1 complete mile?

_____

12. **Algebra** Find the missing value in the equation.

$$\frac{3}{12} + \frac{1}{12} + \frac{?}{12} = \frac{1}{2}$$

A 1   **B** 2   **C** 3   **D** 4

13. There are five people sitting around the dinner table. Each person has $\frac{2}{10}$ of a pie on their plate. How much pie is left? Explain.

_____

_____

_____

Figuring Fractions

1. Joe and Sam shared a cheesecake cut into
12 pieces. Joe ate 3 pieces and Sam ate 5 pieces.
What fraction of the cheesecake did they eat in all?
Show how you found your answer.

_____

2. Kim biked $\frac{1}{5}$ of a mile to Hazel's house and they
both biked $\frac{3}{5}$ of a mile to the library. How far did Kim bike?
Show how you found your answer.

_____

3. Mrs. Green added $\frac{1}{8}$ of a teaspoon of salt to her tomato
sauce. While she was answering the door, Mr. Green
added $\frac{3}{8}$ of a teaspoon of salt to the tomato sauce.
How much salt was added to the tomato sauce? Show how
you found your answer.

_____

4. A pitcher holds 10 glasses of punch. Julia drank 2 glasses
and Bill drank 4 glasses. What fraction of the punch did they
both drink? Show how you found your answer.

_____

5. Scott swam $\frac{1}{4}$ of a mile across the lake to visit a friend.
On the way back, he swam along the shore $\frac{3}{4}$ of a mile.
How far did Scott swim? Show how you found your answer.

_____

6. Ten campers set up their tents alongside a stream. Of the
10 tents, 3 tents are yellow and 2 tents are green. What
fraction of the tents are either yellow or green? Show how
you found your answer.

_____

1. There are 10 campers at Camp Davis. Three campers are swimming, and 2 campers are hiking. What fraction of the campers are swimming or hiking?

   A $\frac{1}{4}$

   B $\frac{1}{3}$

   C $\frac{1}{2}$

   D $\frac{2}{3}$

2. A pencil is $\frac{4}{10}$ of an inch wide. What is $\frac{4}{10}$ written in simplest form?

   A $\frac{2}{10}$

   B $\frac{2}{5}$

   C $\frac{3}{5}$

   D $\frac{8}{10}$

3. What is the sum of $\frac{2}{8} + \frac{4}{8}$ written in simplest form?

   A $\frac{1}{4}$

   B $\frac{3}{8}$

   C $\frac{1}{2}$

   D $\frac{3}{4}$

4. Find the missing value in the equation.

   $\frac{1}{6} + \frac{?}{6} = \frac{5}{6}$

   _____

5. Tracy's soccer team plays 10 games in a season. Each game is 30 minutes long. Explain how you would find the number of hours Tracy's soccer team plays each season.

   _____

   _____

   _____

   _____

   _____

   _____

   _____

Adding Fractions with Like Denominators

When you add fractions with like denominators, add the numerators and keep the denominator the same.

Find the sum of $\frac{3}{8} + \frac{1}{8}$

Add the numerators. $3 + 1 = 4$

Keep the denominator the same. $\frac{3}{8} + \frac{1}{8} = \frac{4}{8}$

Is this fraction expressed in simplest form?

Remember: a fraction is in simplest form when the greatest common factor (GCF) of the numerator and denominator is 1.

$\frac{4 \div 4}{8 \div 4} = \frac{1}{2}$ $\frac{1}{2}$ is in simplest form, because the GCF of 1 and 2 is 1.

Find each sum. Simplify if possible.

1. $\frac{1}{3} + \frac{1}{3}$ _____

2. $\frac{3}{10} + \frac{6}{10}$ _____

3. $\frac{5}{12} + \frac{2}{12}$ _____

4. $\frac{3}{12} + \frac{7}{12}$ _____

5. $\frac{5}{10} + \frac{3}{10}$ _____

6. $\frac{2}{8} + \frac{4}{8}$ _____

7. $\frac{7}{10} + \frac{3}{10}$ _____

8. $\frac{1}{8} + \frac{6}{8}$ _____

9. $\frac{1}{10} + \frac{5}{10}$ _____

10. $\frac{1}{5} + \frac{2}{5} + \frac{2}{5}$ _____

11. $\frac{2}{8} + \frac{1}{8} + \frac{4}{8}$ _____

12. $\frac{2}{6} + \frac{1}{6}$ _____

13. Reasoning There were 10 bowling pins standing before Jared took his first turn. On his first turn, he knocked down 5 pins. On his second turn, he knocked down 3 pins. What fraction of the pins did Jared knock down in his two turns? _____

Adding Fractions with Like Denominators

Find each sum. Simplify if possible.

1. $\frac{2}{5} + \frac{2}{5}$ _____

2. $\frac{4}{10} + \frac{5}{10}$ _____

3. $\frac{3}{8} + \frac{1}{8}$ _____

4. $\frac{3}{6} + \frac{2}{6}$ _____

5. $\frac{2}{10} + \frac{7}{10}$ _____

6. $\frac{5}{8} + \frac{2}{8}$ _____

7. $\frac{1}{6} + \frac{2}{6}$ _____

8. $\frac{9}{12} + \frac{2}{12}$ _____

9. $\frac{4}{12} + \frac{6}{12}$ _____

10. $\frac{2}{12} + \frac{9}{12}$ _____

11. $\frac{1}{8} + \frac{3}{8} + \frac{2}{8}$ _____

12. $\frac{2}{10} + \frac{1}{10} + \frac{5}{10}$ _____

13. $\frac{4}{12} + \frac{2}{12} + \frac{1}{12}$ _____

14. $\frac{2}{5} + \frac{1}{5} + \frac{1}{5}$ _____

15. **Geometry** A side of an equilateral triangle is $\frac{2}{8}$ cm long. Draw a picture that shows the triangle. What is the perimeter of the triangle? _____

16. Of the computer games Lynne owns, $\frac{5}{12}$ are sport games and $\frac{3}{12}$ are educational. What fraction of the games are either sport games or educational games?

   A $\frac{4}{12}$ **B** $\frac{1}{2}$ **C** $\frac{2}{3}$ **D** $\frac{3}{4}$

17. Rob and Nancy are working on a project. Rob completes $\frac{1}{8}$ of it on Monday and $\frac{3}{8}$ of it on Tuesday. Nancy completes $\frac{2}{8}$ of it on Wednesday and $\frac{1}{8}$ of it on Thursday. Is the project complete? Explain.

   _____

   _____

Survey Scores

1. The table shows the results of a fifth-grade class vote. What fraction of the class chose a horse or bird as their favorite pet? Show how you got your answer. Write your answer in simplest form, if possible.

Favorite Pet	Fraction of Student Votes
Horse	$\frac{4}{16}$
Cat	$\frac{3}{16}$
Dog	$\frac{7}{16}$
Bird	$\frac{2}{16}$

_____

2. Using the pet survey, find two pets whose number of votes add up to $\frac{11}{16}$.

_____

3. Darla made a beaded necklace that was $\frac{3}{12}$ of a yard long and a beaded necklace that was $\frac{1}{12}$ of a yard long. What are 3 equivalent fractions for the total length of Darla's necklaces?

_____

4. The table shows the results of a survey of cousins. What fraction of the cousins chose ice cream or fruit as their favorite dessert? Explain how you got your answer. Write your answer in simplest form, if possible.

Favorite Dessert	Fraction of Cousins Who Voted
Ice cream	$\frac{2}{12}$
Brownies	$\frac{5}{12}$
Cookies	$\frac{2}{12}$
Fruit	$\frac{1}{12}$

_____

5. Using the dessert survey, find two desserts whose numbers of votes add up to $\frac{7}{12}$.

_____

Name _____

1. Marti has 6 shirts. Two shirts are pink and 1 is red. What fraction of Marti's shirts are pink or red?

A $\frac{1}{4}$

B $\frac{1}{3}$

C $\frac{1}{2}$

D $\frac{2}{3}$

2. Jack wrote this equation on the board, but Kim erased part of it.

$$\frac{3}{12} + \frac{\square}{12} = \frac{7}{12}$$

What is the value of the missing numerator?

A 4

B 5

C 10

D 12

3. In the regular polygon below, all sides are the same length. What is its perimeter? (Remember, perimeter equals the distance around a figure.)

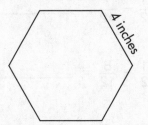

4 inches

A 16 inches

B 20 inches

C 24 inches

D 28 inches

4. What is the sum of $\frac{2}{10} + \frac{1}{10} + \frac{3}{10}$ in simplest form?

_____

5. **Estimation** Josie read 246 pages of a book last month. Her older brother says he read about 3 to 4 times as many pages as Josie. Explain why 2,500 is NOT a reasonable estimate for the number of pages that Josie's brother read.

_____

_____

_____

_____

_____

_____

_____

Modeling Subtraction of Fractions

Karla made a pizza and cut it into 10 slices. She ate two slices.
What fraction of the pizza is left?

You can use a model to subtract fractions.

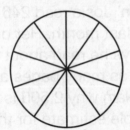

Karla's pizza is divided into 10 slices. One way to show
this is $\frac{10}{10} = 1$ whole pizza. Karla ate two slices of the pizza.
Cross out two of the slices. Count the number of slices left.
There are 8 slices or $\frac{8}{10}$ of the pizza left.

$$\frac{10}{10} - \frac{2}{10} = \frac{8}{10}$$

Write the answer in simplest form, if possible.

$$\frac{8 \div 2}{10 \div 2} = \frac{4}{5}$$

Use fraction strips or models to subtract. Simplify if possible.

1. $\frac{5}{5} - \frac{2}{5} =$ _____

2. $\frac{7}{10} - \frac{3}{10} =$ _____

3. $\frac{3}{4} - \frac{2}{4} =$ _____

4. $\frac{8}{10} - \frac{5}{10} =$ _____

5. $\frac{6}{6} - \frac{3}{6} =$ _____

6. $\frac{11}{12} - \frac{7}{12} =$ _____

7. $\frac{5}{6} - \frac{2}{6} =$ _____

8. $\frac{4}{8} - \frac{2}{8} =$ _____

9. $\frac{11}{12} - \frac{8}{12} =$ _____

10. $\frac{7}{12} - \frac{5}{12} =$ _____

11. $\frac{6}{10} - \frac{4}{10} =$ _____

12. $\frac{9}{12} - \frac{6}{12} =$ _____

13. **Algebra** Find x.

$$x - \frac{1}{6} = \frac{1}{6}$$ _____

Modeling Subtraction of Fractions

Use fraction strips to subtract. Simplify if possible.

1. $\frac{11}{12} - \frac{5}{12}$ _____

2. $\frac{6}{12} - \frac{4}{12}$ _____

3. $\frac{1}{2} - \frac{1}{2}$ _____

4. $\frac{4}{6} - \frac{1}{6}$ _____

5. $\frac{5}{6} - \frac{4}{6}$ _____

6. $\frac{9}{10} - \frac{3}{10}$ _____

7. $\frac{5}{8} - \frac{2}{8}$ _____

8. $\frac{7}{8} - \frac{5}{8}$ _____

9. $\frac{3}{4} - \frac{2}{4}$ _____

10. $\frac{3}{5} - \frac{2}{5}$ _____

11. $\frac{2}{5} - \frac{1}{5}$ _____

12. $\frac{9}{12} - \frac{1}{12}$ _____

13. **Algebra** Evaluate $\frac{5}{8} - ? = \frac{3}{8}$. _____

14. **Draw a Diagram** Harriet has $\frac{3}{4}$ tank of gas left in her car.
    If she needs $\frac{1}{4}$ tank to go to her friend's house and another
    $\frac{1}{4}$ tank to get back home, does she have enough gas?
    Draw a diagram and explain your answer.

    _____

    _____

15. Alicia had $\frac{10}{12}$ yard of fabric. She used $\frac{8}{12}$ for a pillow. How much
    fabric did she have left? Explain how you found your answer.

    _____

    _____

Agility Fun Run

The dog agility Fun Run is about to begin. Answer the
Fun Run questions below. Simplify, if possible.

1. Twelve dogs raced up and down the A-frame.
    Three dogs did not touch the contact zone on the
    down side and were disqualified. What fraction
    of these dogs remains in the Fun Run?   _____

2. Ten dogs raced through the tunnel. Four dogs
    entered through the wrong end and were disqualified.
    What fraction of these dogs remains in the Fun Run?   _____

3. Six dogs leapt over the triple jump bars. Three dogs knocked
    down the top bar and were disqualified. What fraction of
    these dogs remains in the Fun Run?   _____

4. Eight dogs raced up and down the walk-on ramp.
    Five dogs did not touch the contact zone on the up
    side and were disqualified. What fraction of these
    dogs remains in the Fun Run?   _____

5. Six dogs ran up and down the seesaw. Two dogs
    jumped off before the seesaw touched the ground
    and were disqualified. What fraction of these dogs
    remains in the Fun Run?   _____

6. Five dogs zoomed through the tire jump. One dog
    knocked the tire frame over and was disqualified.
    What fraction of these dogs remains in the Fun Run?   _____

7. Ten dogs were headed over to a new event but five of
    them went to take a break and get water. What fraction
    of these dogs went to take a break?   _____

Name _____

1. The map shows David's campsite, the park ranger's cabin, and Badger lake at Hundred Pines State Park.

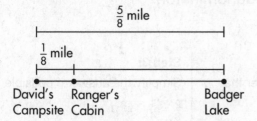

What is the distance from the ranger's cabin to Badger Lake expressed in simplest form?

A $\frac{1}{8}$ mile

B $\frac{1}{2}$ mile

C $\frac{5}{8}$ mile

D $\frac{3}{4}$ mile

2. David hikes from his campsite to the ranger's cabin and then back to his campsite. How far does David hike?

A $\frac{1}{2}$ mile

B $\frac{3}{8}$ mile

C $\frac{1}{4}$ mile

D $\frac{1}{8}$ mile

3. What is the sum of $\frac{3}{8} + \frac{1}{8}$ written in simplest form?

A $\frac{1}{8}$

B $\frac{1}{4}$

C $\frac{1}{2}$

D $\frac{2}{3}$

4. Find the sum.

$$\frac{1}{12} + \frac{4}{12}$$

_____

5. Ethan is 3 inches taller than Daisy. Let x = Ethan's height. Write an expression that represents Daisy's height. Explain how you knew what operation to use in your expression.

_____

_____

_____

_____

Subtracting Fractions with Like Denominators

When subtracting with two fractions having the same denominator, the difference also has the same denominator.

Find $\frac{7}{8} - \frac{5}{8}$.

Step 1:
Subtract the numerators.

$7 - 5 = 2$

Step 2:
Write the difference over the same denominator.

$\frac{7}{8} - \frac{5}{8} = \frac{2}{8}$

Step 3:
Simplify the answer if possible.

$\frac{2}{8} = \frac{1}{4}$

So, $\frac{7}{8} - \frac{5}{8} = \frac{1}{4}$.

Subtract the fractions. Simplify if possible.

1. $\frac{4}{5} - \frac{3}{5}$ _____

2. $\frac{8}{12} - \frac{3}{12}$ _____

3. $\frac{3}{6} - \frac{1}{6}$ _____

4. $\frac{9}{10} - \frac{3}{10}$ _____

5. $\frac{11}{12} - \frac{5}{12}$ _____

6. $\frac{5}{6} - \frac{1}{6}$ _____

7. $\frac{97}{100} - \frac{40}{100}$ _____

8. $\frac{5}{8} - \frac{1}{8}$ _____

9. $\frac{7}{10} - \frac{2}{10} - \frac{1}{10}$ _____

10. $\frac{7}{12} - \frac{4}{12}$ _____

11. $\frac{3}{4} - \frac{1}{4} - \frac{2}{4}$ _____

12. $\frac{8}{8} - \frac{1}{8}$ _____

13. **Reasoning** During archery practice, Manny hit the target 7 times out of 10 tries. What fraction of his arrows did NOT hit the target?

_____

Subtracting Fractions with Like Denominators

In **1** through **12**, find each difference. Simplify if possible.

1. $\frac{4}{5} - \frac{1}{5}$ _____

2. $\frac{9}{10} - \frac{5}{10}$ _____

3. $\frac{5}{8} - \frac{2}{8}$ _____

4. $\frac{6}{8} - \frac{2}{8}$ _____

5. $\frac{9}{10} - \frac{8}{10}$ _____

6. $\frac{9}{12} - \frac{5}{12}$ _____

7. $\frac{5}{6} - \frac{3}{6}$ _____

8. $\frac{3}{4} - \frac{1}{4}$ _____

9. $\frac{6}{8} - \frac{4}{8}$ _____

10. $\frac{7}{12} - \frac{3}{12}$ _____

11. $\frac{10}{12} - \frac{6}{12}$ _____

12. $\frac{4}{6} - \frac{4}{6}$ _____

13. **Geometry** The area of rectangle A is $\frac{11}{12}$ square meters. The area of rectangle B is $\frac{8}{12}$ square meters. How much larger is rectangle A? _____

14. Joan counted that $\frac{2}{10}$ of her jelly beans were red. Dean counted that $\frac{6}{10}$ of his jelly beans were red. How much greater a fraction of Dean's jelly beans were red? _____

15. **Think About the Process** On the weekends, Paul jogs $\frac{9}{10}$ mile. On the weekdays, Paul jogs $\frac{5}{10}$ mile. Which expression shows how many more miles Paul jogs on the weekends than on a weekday?

A $\frac{9}{10} + \frac{5}{10}$ B $\frac{9}{10} - \frac{5}{10}$ C $\frac{5}{10} + \frac{9}{10}$ D $\frac{5}{10} - \frac{9}{10}$

16. In a classroom, $\frac{2}{12}$ of the students play baseball, $\frac{4}{12}$ play football, $\frac{1}{12}$ are in the chorus, and the rest participate in volunteer programs. What fraction of the students participate in volunteer programs? Explain your answer.

_____

_____

_____

_____

Cooking Up Fractions

1. A brownie recipe calls for $\frac{2}{3}$ cup of chocolate chips for each pan of brownies. Nadine has 1 cup of chips. Does she have enough chocolate chips to make 2 pans of brownies? Explain.

   _____

   _____

2. In the question above, if Nadine's neighbor gave her 2 cups of chocolate chips, would she have enough chocolate chips to make 3 pans of brownies? Explain.

   _____

   _____

3. Tim's oatmeal cookie recipe calls for $\frac{7}{12}$ of a cup of oatmeal. Tim only has $\frac{5}{12}$ of a cup of oatmeal. How much more oatmeal does he need to make the cookies?   _____

4. There are 14 cake decorations in a box: $\frac{7}{14}$ are ballerinas, $\frac{3}{14}$ clowns, and $\frac{4}{14}$ pandas. Jacob takes 2 of the decorations. What fraction of decorations are left in the box?   _____

5. Tanya baked 12 cheesecakes. She will garnish each with fresh fruit: $\frac{3}{12}$ with strawberries, $\frac{6}{12}$ with blueberries, and $\frac{3}{12}$ with cherries. After Tanya garnishes 3 of the cheesecakes, what fraction of cheesecakes remain to be garnished with fruit?   _____

6. The Bluebell Cooking School's cake decorating class is $\frac{4}{10}$ full. What fraction of the class is still open to students? Show your work.   _____

Name _____

1. Of the 12 books on Marco's shelf, 9 are about music or computers. The rest are nature books. What fraction of Marco's books are about nature?

   A $\frac{1}{4}$

   B $\frac{1}{3}$

   C $\frac{2}{3}$

   D $\frac{3}{4}$

2. The table shows the amount of time four people spend exercising.

   Exercise Log

Name	Time
Bill	$\frac{1}{2}$ hour
Carly	$\frac{3}{4}$ hour
Dimitri	$\frac{2}{3}$ hour
Emma	$\frac{2}{8}$ hour

   Which person exercises for the least amount of time?

   A Bill

   B Carly

   C Dimitri

   D Emma

3. What fraction is represented by point M on the number line below?

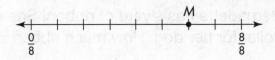

   A $\frac{1}{2}$

   B $\frac{2}{3}$

   C $\frac{3}{4}$

   D $\frac{4}{5}$

4. What is the difference of $\frac{5}{6} - \frac{1}{6} - \frac{2}{6}$ in simplest form?

   _____

5. The numbers in this list follow a pattern. Write the missing number. Then describe the pattern you found.

   0 3 6 9 ____ 15 18 21

   _____

   _____

Adding and Subtracting on the Number Line

Bernadette has $\frac{7}{8}$ yard of ribbon. She cuts off $\frac{3}{8}$ yard to make a collar for her dog. How much ribbon does Bernadette have left?

You can use a number line to help you subtract fractions.

Draw a number line to represent the ribbon. Divide the number line into eighths. Place a point at $\frac{7}{8}$ to show the length of the ribbon before it is cut. Draw an arrow $\frac{3}{8}$ of a unit to the left to show how much of the ribbon Bernadette cut off.

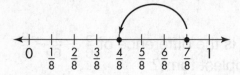

$\frac{7}{8} - \frac{3}{8} = \frac{4}{8}$ Simplify: $\frac{4}{8} = \frac{1}{2}$ There is $\frac{1}{2}$ yard of ribbon left.

You can also use a number line to help you add fractions.

Kevin and Duane are recycling aluminum cans. Each boy has collected $\frac{4}{10}$ pound. How many pounds have they collected in all?

Divide this number line into tenths. Start at zero and draw an arrow to and place a point at $\frac{4}{10}$ to show the amount of aluminum Kevin collected. Now draw another arrow $\frac{4}{10}$ of a unit long to the right to show Duane's amount.

$\frac{4}{10} + \frac{4}{10} = \frac{8}{10}$ Simplify: $\frac{8}{10} = \frac{4}{5}$ The boys collected $\frac{4}{5}$ pound of aluminum.

Add or subtract the fractions. You may use a number line. Simplify your answer, if possible.

1. $\frac{2}{5} + \frac{1}{5} =$ _____

2. $\frac{8}{12} - \frac{3}{12} =$ _____

3. $\frac{5}{10} - \frac{3}{10} =$ _____

4. $\frac{2}{6} + \frac{1}{6} =$ _____

5. $\frac{29}{100} - \frac{4}{100} =$ _____

6. $\frac{1}{8} + \frac{2}{8} + \frac{3}{8} =$ _____

Adding and Subtracting on the Number Line

Write the equation shown by each number line.
Write your answer. Simplify if possible.

1.

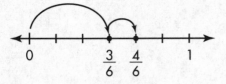

_____

2.

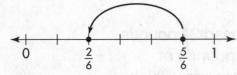

_____

Draw a number line to solve. Simplify if possible.

3. $\frac{3}{8} + \frac{2}{8}$ _____

4. $\frac{9}{12} - \frac{3}{12}$ _____

5. Draw a Diagram Ann is growing two different plants for a science project. Plant A grew $\frac{4}{12}$ inch the first week and $\frac{2}{12}$ inch the second week. Plant B grew $\frac{7}{12}$ inch the first week and did not grow after that. Show the heights of each plant on a different number line. Which plant is taller now?

_____

6. Which equation is represented by the number line below?

A $\frac{1}{4} + \frac{2}{4} = \frac{3}{4}$ **B** $\frac{1}{4} + \frac{3}{4} = \frac{4}{4}$ **C** $\frac{1}{4} + \frac{1}{4} = \frac{2}{4}$ **D** $\frac{1}{3} + \frac{1}{3} = \frac{2}{3}$

7. Dave made fruit punch for his party but accidentally tripped and spilled $\frac{5}{12}$ of the punch. How much of the punch was left? Explain how you found your answer.

_____

Number Lines

1. In the dog-walk fundraiser for the humane society, Tanya walked $2\frac{3}{4}$ miles, Bruce walked $2\frac{1}{2}$ miles, and Jack walked $2\frac{7}{8}$ miles. Show these distances on the number line. Who walked the farthest?

_____

2. Carl made a salad for the school picnic. He used $3\frac{7}{8}$ pounds of cucumbers, $3\frac{3}{4}$ pounds of lettuce, and $3\frac{5}{8}$ pounds of tomatoes. Show these amounts on the number line. Which salad ingredient weighed the most?

_____

3. Jefferson was putting the following fractions on a number line: $\frac{1}{2}$, $\frac{1}{3}$, $\frac{5}{6}$, $\frac{8}{12}$. How should he order this set of fractions from least to greatest? Explain how Jefferson would find his answer.

_____

_____

_____

_____

4. Rachel labeled a number line by tenths. She wrote from $\frac{1}{10}$ through $\frac{9}{10}$ and put a point at each tenth. Between which two points should she place $\frac{1}{2}$?

_____

Name _____

1. The model is shaded to represent a fraction.

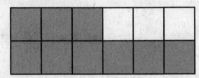

Which of the following is an equivalent fraction?

A $\frac{3}{12}$

B $\frac{3}{9}$

C $\frac{3}{4}$

D $\frac{9}{3}$

2. Estimation Each of the three fourth-grade classes at Woodrow Wilson Elementary has 22 students. About how many students are in all three classes?

A 90

B 60

C 30

D 25

3. Mental Math Angel bought 5 books for $45. How much did each book cost if each book was the same price?

A $5

B $6

C $8

D $9

4. Jamie has seen her favorite movie 95 times! Derrek has seen it 113 times! How many more times has Derrek seen the movie?

_____

5. A number has a 4 in the thousands place, a 1 in the tens place, a 0 in the ones place, and a 9 in the hundreds place. What is the number?

_____

6. Find the product of 29×3.

_____

Improper Fractions and Mixed Numbers

You can use fraction strips to write a mixed number as an improper fraction.

$3\frac{1}{2}$ of the model below is shaded.

$\frac{1}{2}$	$\frac{1}{2}$
$\frac{1}{2}$	$\frac{1}{2}$
$\frac{1}{2}$	$\frac{1}{2}$
$\frac{1}{2}$	$\frac{1}{2}$

Into how many parts is each strip divided? 2. This is your denominator.

Count the shaded halves. There are 7. This is your numerator.

$3\frac{1}{2}$ is the same as the improper fraction $\frac{7}{2}$.

You can also use fraction strips to write an improper fraction as a mixed number.

$\frac{8}{3}$ of the model below is shaded.

$\frac{1}{3}$	$\frac{1}{3}$	$\frac{1}{3}$
$\frac{1}{3}$	$\frac{1}{3}$	$\frac{1}{3}$
$\frac{1}{3}$	$\frac{1}{3}$	$\frac{1}{3}$

How many strips are completely shaded? 2. This is your whole number.

What fraction of the third strip is shaded? $\frac{2}{3}$. This is your fraction.

$\frac{8}{3}$ is the same as the mixed number $2\frac{2}{3}$.

Write each mixed number as an improper fraction.

1. $2\frac{1}{3}$ _____

2. $4\frac{1}{5}$ _____

3. $2\frac{3}{4}$ _____

4. $5\frac{2}{6}$ _____

Write each improper fraction as a mixed number or a whole number.

5. $\frac{13}{12}$ _____

6. $\frac{50}{10}$ _____

7. $\frac{23}{10}$ _____

8. $\frac{17}{8}$ _____

9. **Writing to Explain** Is $\frac{45}{5}$ equal to a whole number or a mixed number? Explain how you know.

_____

_____

_____

Improper Fractions and Mixed Numbers

Write each mixed number as an improper fraction.

1. $3\frac{2}{5}$ _____   **2.** $6\frac{1}{4}$ _____   **3.** $2\frac{1}{12}$ _____   **4.** $2\frac{7}{10}$ _____

Write each improper fraction as a mixed number or whole number.

5. $\frac{12}{5}$ _____   **6.** $\frac{24}{3}$ _____   **7.** $\frac{32}{3}$ _____   **8.** $\frac{20}{12}$ _____

9. Number Sense Matt had to write $3\frac{4}{12}$ as an improper fraction. Write how you would tell Matt the easiest way to do so.

_____

_____

_____

_____

10. Jill has $\frac{11}{8}$ ounces of trail mix. Write the weight of Jill's trail mix as a mixed number. _____

11. Nick had $1\frac{3}{4}$ gal of milk. Write the amount of milk Nick has as an improper fraction. _____

12. Which is **NOT** an improper fraction equal to 8?

A $\frac{24}{3}$ **B** $\frac{42}{6}$ **C** $\frac{32}{4}$ **D** $\frac{64}{8}$

13. Writing to Explain Write three different improper fractions that equal $4\frac{1}{2}$. (Hint: find equivalent fractions.)

_____

_____

Recreation Time!

1. Timothy has computer class 3 times a week.
Each class is 45 minutes long. How many hours of
computer class does Timothy have per week?
In 4 weeks? _____

2. Alex practices soccer 4 times a week for 50 minutes
each practice. How many total hours does Alex
practice soccer per week? In 2 weeks? _____

3. Laurel went swimming 7 times in 3 weeks. One
time she swam for $1\frac{1}{2}$ hours. The other 6 times she
swam for 30 minutes each time. How many hours
did Laurel swim in 3 weeks? _____

4. Caitlin, Cindy, and Connie went jogging at
the recreation center. Caitlin jogged for 40 minutes,
Cindy jogged for 30 minutes, and Connie jogged
for 70 minutes. What was the total amount of
time they jogged altogether? _____

5. Dena takes karate classes every Tuesday and
Thursday. Each class is 55 minutes long. How
many hours of class will Dena have in 3 weeks? _____

6. Jack spent $9\frac{3}{4}$ hours practicing ice hockey with
his team. How many $\frac{1}{4}$ hours is that? _____

7. Misa takes 3 dance classes each week. Ballet
class is 45 minutes long, modern dance is 50 minutes
long, and jazz dance is 35 minutes long. How
many hours of dance class does Misa have in
2 weeks? _____

8. Carlos practices piano every Monday, Wednesday,
and Friday for 35 minutes each day. He also
practices guitar every Tuesday, Thursday, and
Saturday for 30 minutes each day. How many hours
does Carlos spend practicing musical instruments
each week? _____

Name _____

1. It takes 4 pounds of grapes to make 1 pound of raisins. How many pounds of grapes would you need to make 3,000 pounds of raisins?

   A   1,000 pounds

   B   6,000 pounds

   C   9,000 pounds

   D   12,000 pounds

2. What number represents *n* in the diagram below?

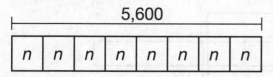

   A   7

   B   80

   C   700

   D   800

3. What equation is modeled with this number line?

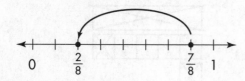

   A $\frac{7}{8} - \frac{5}{8} = \frac{2}{8}$

   B $\frac{7}{10} - \frac{5}{10} = \frac{2}{10}$

   C $\frac{2}{8} + \frac{5}{8} = \frac{7}{8}$

   D $\frac{2}{10} + \frac{5}{10} = \frac{7}{10}$

4. What is the sum of $\frac{9}{10}$ and $\frac{1}{10}$?

   _____

5. Jen needs to save $180 for a new camping tent. She is able to save $9 each week. How many weeks will Jen need to save to reach her goal? Draw a picture and write an equation to solve the problem. Explain how you found your answer.

   _____

   _____

   _____

   _____

   _____

   _____

   _____

Modeling Addition and Subtraction of Mixed Numbers

Example 1: Draw a model to add $1\frac{7}{8} + 2\frac{3}{8}$.

Step 1 Model each mixed number using fraction strips.

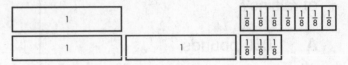

Step 2 Add the fractions. Regroup if you can.

$$\frac{7}{8}$$
$$+ \frac{3}{8}$$
$$\frac{10}{8} = 1\frac{2}{8}$$

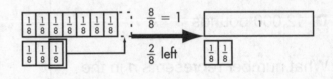

$\frac{8}{8} = 1$

$\frac{2}{8}$ left

Step 3 Add the whole numbers to the regrouped fractions. Write the sum. Simplify, if possible.

So, $1\frac{7}{8} + 2\frac{3}{8} = 4\frac{1}{4}$.

Example 2: Draw a model to subtract $2\frac{1}{5} - 1\frac{2}{5}$.

Step 1 Model the number you are subtracting from, $2\frac{1}{5}$.

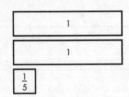

Step 2 Rename $2\frac{1}{5}$ as $1\frac{6}{5}$. Cross out one whole and $\frac{2}{5}$ to show subtracting $1\frac{2}{5}$.

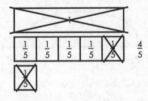

$\frac{4}{5}$

Express the part of the model that is not crossed out as a fraction or mixed number. So, $2\frac{1}{5} - 1\frac{2}{5} = \frac{4}{5}$.

Use fraction strips to find each sum or difference. Simplify, if possible.

1. $3\frac{1}{2} + 1\frac{1}{2}$ **2.** $2\frac{5}{8} + 4\frac{3}{8}$ **3.** $5\frac{2}{6} + 3\frac{5}{6}$ **4.** $2\frac{2}{4} + 6\frac{3}{4}$

5. $6\frac{1}{8} - 3\frac{5}{8}$ **6.** $8\frac{3}{12} - 2\frac{5}{12}$ **7.** $12\frac{1}{3} - 5\frac{2}{3}$ **8.** $9\frac{7}{10} - 6\frac{9}{10}$

Modeling Addition and Subtraction of Mixed Numbers

For **1** and **2**, use each model to find each sum or difference.

1. $1\frac{3}{8} + 1\frac{7}{8}$

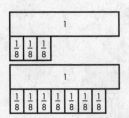

2. $3\frac{1}{5} - 1\frac{4}{5}$

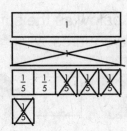

Use fraction strips to find each sum or difference.
Simplify, if possible.

3. $2\frac{1}{3} + 1\frac{2}{3}$ **4.** $3\frac{5}{6} + 4\frac{3}{6}$ **5.** $5\frac{1}{4} - 1\frac{2}{4}$ **6.** $12\frac{3}{8} - 2\frac{5}{8}$

7. $8\frac{1}{6} - 3\frac{5}{6}$ **8.** $4\frac{6}{10} + 5\frac{7}{10}$ **9.** $7\frac{1}{3} - 4\frac{2}{3}$ **10.** $6\frac{2}{5} + 3\frac{4}{5}$

11. $1\frac{1}{6} + 3\frac{5}{6}$ **12.** $2\frac{4}{8} + 6\frac{7}{8}$ **13.** $6\frac{3}{5} - 4\frac{3}{5}$ **14.** $5\frac{1}{3} - 4\frac{2}{3}$

15. Jerome's rain gauge showed $13\frac{9}{10}$ centimeters (cm) at the end of last month. At the end of this month, the rain gauge showed $15\frac{3}{10}$ centimeters. How many more centimeters of rain fell this month?

A $29\frac{2}{10}$ cm   **B** $15\frac{3}{10}$ cm   **C** $2\frac{4}{10}$ cm   **D** $1\frac{4}{10}$ cm

16. You are adding $3\frac{2}{3} + 2\frac{2}{3}$ using fraction strips. Explain how you rename the fraction part of the problem.

_____

_____

Prime Time

Remember that a prime number is a whole number greater than
1 that has exactly two factors, itself and 1.

Every number greater than 5 can be written as the sum of three
prime numbers. For example, 13 can be written as the sum of
3 + 3 + 7.

Express the numbers below as the sum of three prime numbers.
Write the primes in the squares.

1. ☐ + ☐ + ☐ = 17

2. ☐ + ☐ + ☐ = 10

3. ☐ + ☐ + ☐ = 15

4. ☐ + ☐ + ☐ = 21

5. ☐ + ☐ + ☐ = 32

6. ☐ + ☐ + ☐ = 30

7. ☐ + ☐ + ☐ = 26

8. ☐ + ☐ + ☐ = 50

Name _____

1. Find the difference. Simplify, if possible.

$$\frac{4}{12} - \frac{1}{12}$$

A $\frac{1}{12}$

B $\frac{2}{12}$

C $\frac{1}{4}$

D $\frac{1}{3}$

2. After Ronaldo's Fourth of July party, $\frac{4}{6}$ of his cake is left. How much cake will be left after his cousin Max eats another $\frac{1}{6}$? Simplify your answer if possible.

A $\frac{5}{6}$

B $\frac{1}{2}$

C $\frac{1}{3}$

D $\frac{3}{12}$

3. Noreen bought two shirts for $13 each and two pairs of shoes for $18 a pair. How much did she pay in all?

A $31

B $44

C $49

D $62

4. A day pass at a theme park costs $16 for a child and $24 for an adult. How much would it cost to get day passes for 1 adult and 2 children?

_____

5. Kirk, Tanya, Ben, Maya, and Rico equally share 3 apples. What fraction of an apple does each person get?

A $\frac{1}{3}$

B $\frac{3}{8}$

C $\frac{3}{5}$

D $\frac{5}{8}$

Adding Mixed Numbers

Randy talks on the telephone for $2\frac{5}{6}$ hours, and then surfs the Internet for $3\frac{3}{4}$ hours. How many hours does he spend on the two activities?

Step 1. Write equivalent fractions with the least common denominator. You can use fraction strips to show the equivalent fractions.

$$3\frac{3}{4} = 3\frac{9}{12}$$

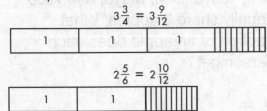

$$2\frac{5}{6} = 2\frac{10}{12}$$

Step 2. Add the fraction part of the mixed number first. Then add the whole numbers.

$$\frac{9}{12} + \frac{10}{12} = \frac{19}{12}$$

$$3 + 2 = 5$$

$$\frac{19}{12} + 5 = 5\frac{19}{12}$$

Step 3. Simplify the sum if possible.

$$5\frac{19}{12} = 6\frac{7}{12} \text{ hours}$$

So, $2\frac{5}{6} + 3\frac{3}{4} = 6\frac{7}{12}$.

In **1** through **6**, find each sum. Simplify if possible.

1. $2\frac{10}{12}$
   $+ 3\frac{3}{12}$
   _____

2. $1\frac{3}{8}$
   $+ 6\frac{6}{8}$
   _____

3. $5\frac{4}{10}$
   $+ 4\frac{2}{10}$
   _____

4. $10\frac{2}{6} + \frac{3}{6} =$ _____

5. $3\frac{3}{12} + 6\frac{8}{12} =$ _____

6. $1\frac{2}{5} + 3\frac{1}{5} =$ _____

7. **Geometry** Tirzah wants to put a fence around her garden. She has 22 yards of fence material. Does she have enough to go all the way around the garden?

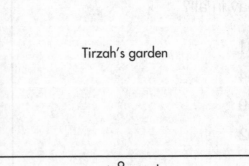

Tirzah's garden

$4\frac{8}{12}$ yards

$6\frac{9}{12}$ yards

_____

_____

_____

Adding Mixed Numbers

In **1** through **6**, find each sum. Simplify, if possible. Estimate for reasonableness.

1. $7\frac{2}{6} + 8\frac{5}{6}$ _____

2. $4\frac{3}{4} + 2\frac{2}{4}$ _____

3. $11\frac{9}{10} + 3\frac{2}{10}$ _____

4. $7\frac{9}{8} + 5\frac{2}{8}$ _____

5. $5\frac{8}{12} + 3\frac{5}{12}$ _____

6. $21\frac{11}{12} + 17\frac{5}{12}$ _____

7. Number Sense Write two mixed numbers that have a sum of 3.

_____

8. What is the total measure of an average man's brain and heart in kilograms (kg)?

_____

Vital Organ Measures

Average woman's brain	$1\frac{3}{10}$ kg	$2\frac{8}{10}$ lb
Average man's brain	$1\frac{4}{10}$ kg	3 lb
Average human heart	$\frac{3}{10}$ kg	$\frac{7}{10}$ lb

9. What is the total weight of an average woman's brain and heart in pounds (lb)? _____

10. What is the sum of the measures of an average man's brain and an average woman's brain in kilograms? _____

11. Which is a good comparison of the estimated sum and the actual sum of $7\frac{9}{12} + 2\frac{11}{12}$?

A Estimated $<$ actual

C Actual $>$ estimated

B Actual $=$ estimated

D Estimated $>$ actual

12. Can the sum of two mixed numbers be equal to 2? Explain why or why not.

_____

_____

_____

Mixed Sums

1. Annie walked her dog $2\frac{1}{4}$ miles from her house to the dog park and $3\frac{7}{8}$ miles around the park. Then she walked the same distance home. How many miles did she walk in all?

   _____

2. John's full backpack weighs $5\frac{1}{2}$ pounds, and Tyrone's full backpack weighs $6\frac{3}{5}$ pounds. What is the total weight of both boys' backpacks?

   _____

3. Julie has two extension cords with lengths of $22\frac{1}{6}$ feet and $26\frac{3}{4}$ feet. How long a cord can she make by attaching them together?

   _____

4. Terry weighed his two cats at the veterinarian's office. Boots weighed $12\frac{9}{10}$ pounds, and Tiger weighed $13\frac{1}{4}$ pounds. What is the total weight of both cats?

   _____

5. David ran $9\frac{3}{4}$ miles on Saturday and $7\frac{1}{10}$ miles on Sunday. How many miles did he run on the weekend?

   _____

6. Amanda's library books weigh $4\frac{3}{8}$ pounds, and her water bottle weighs $1\frac{7}{16}$ pounds. What is the total weight of her books and water bottle?

   _____

1. What number is missing from the pattern?

| 201 | 403 | ? | 807 | 1,009 |

   A 205

   B 405

   C 605

   D 607

2. Neil spends $1\frac{2}{8}$ hours washing the car and $2\frac{5}{8}$ hours mowing and weeding the yard. How many total hours does he spend on his chores? Simplify your answer if possible.

   A $3\frac{3}{8}$ hours

   B $3\frac{5}{8}$ hours

   C $3\frac{6}{8}$ hours

   D $3\frac{7}{8}$ hours

3. Which of the fractions is equivalent to $\frac{2}{3}$?

   A $\frac{8}{12}$

   B $\frac{6}{10}$

   C $\frac{4}{8}$

   D $\frac{2}{5}$

4. Mr. DeWitt carved a wooden boat for his granddaughter. He began with a piece of wood that was 203 centimeters long. The boat is 167 centimeters long. How many centimeters did Mr. DeWitt carve off the length of the wood when he made the boat?

_____

5. **Estimation** The distance between Miami and Naples is 107 miles. The distance between Miami and Jacksonville is about three times this distance. Landon estimates that the distance between Miami and Jacksonville is about 400 miles. Is Landon's estimate reasonable? Why or why not?

_____

_____

_____

_____

_____

_____

_____

Subtracting Mixed Numbers

The Plainville Zoo has had elephants for $12\frac{4}{6}$ years. The zoo has had zebras for $5\frac{3}{6}$ years. How many years longer has the zoo had elephants?

Step 1: Write equivalent fractions with the least common denominator. You can use fraction strips.

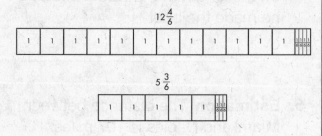

Step 2: Find the difference of $12\frac{4}{6} - 5\frac{3}{6}$. Subtract the fractions. Then subtract the whole numbers. Simplify the difference if possible.

$$\frac{4}{6} - \frac{3}{6} = \frac{1}{6} \qquad\qquad 12 - 5 = 7$$

So, $12\frac{4}{6} - 5\frac{3}{6} = 7\frac{1}{6}$ years.

Example 2: Sometimes you may have to rename a fraction so you can subtract. Find the difference of $6 - 2\frac{3}{8}$.

$$
\begin{array}{ccccc}
6 & \longrightarrow & \text{rename} & \longrightarrow & 5\frac{8}{8} \\
-2\frac{3}{8} & & & & -2\frac{3}{8} \\
\hline
& & & & 3\frac{5}{8}
\end{array}
$$

For **1** through **4**, find each difference. Simplify, if possible.
Remember: You may have to rename a fraction in order to subtract.

1. $\quad 4\frac{5}{8}$
$\quad -2\frac{2}{8}$
_____

2. $\quad 5\frac{7}{12}$
$\quad -1\frac{2}{12}$
_____

3. $\quad 3$
$\quad -1\frac{3}{4}$
_____

4. $\quad 6\frac{5}{6}$
$\quad -5\frac{4}{6}$
_____

5. Number Sense To find the difference of $7 - 3\frac{5}{12}$, how do you rename the 7?

_____

6. Robyn ran $5\frac{3}{4}$ miles last week. She ran $4\frac{1}{4}$ miles this week. How many more miles did she run last week?

Name _____

Subtracting Mixed Numbers

For **1** through **10**, find each difference. Simplify, if possible.

1. $10\frac{3}{4}$
    $- 7\frac{1}{4}$
    ‾‾‾‾‾‾

2. $7\frac{4}{6}$
    $- 2\frac{3}{6}$
    ‾‾‾‾‾‾

3. 3
    $- 2\frac{2}{3}$
    ‾‾‾‾‾‾

4. $17\frac{8}{12}$
    $- 12\frac{3}{12}$
    ‾‾‾‾‾‾

5. $9\frac{2}{6} - 6\frac{5}{6}$ _____

6. $4\frac{1}{5} - 2\frac{3}{5}$ _____

7. $6\frac{3}{12} - 3\frac{4}{12}$ _____

8. $5\frac{2}{8} - 3\frac{7}{8}$ _____

9. $8\frac{1}{4} - 7\frac{3}{4}$ _____

10. $2\frac{9}{10} - 2\frac{5}{10}$ _____

Strategy Practice The table shows the length and width of several kinds of bird eggs.

11. How much longer is the Canada goose egg than the raven egg?

_____

12. How much wider is the turtledove egg than the robin egg?

_____

Egg Sizes in Inches (in.)

Bird	Length	Width
Canada goose	$3\frac{4}{10}$	$2\frac{3}{10}$
Robin	$\frac{8}{10}$	$\frac{6}{10}$
Turtledove	$1\frac{2}{10}$	$\frac{9}{10}$
Raven	$1\frac{9}{10}$	$1\frac{3}{10}$

13. Which is the difference of $21\frac{1}{4} - 18\frac{2}{4}$?

A $2\frac{1}{4}$　　　B $2\frac{2}{4}$　　　C $2\frac{3}{4}$　　　D $3\frac{1}{4}$

14. Explain why it is necessary to rename $4\frac{1}{4}$ if you subtract $\frac{3}{4}$ from it.

_____

_____

_____

Mixed Differences

Answer each question. Write your answers in simplest form.

1. Jenna bought a spool of ribbon for her craft projects. It contained $5\frac{3}{4}$ meters of ribbon. She used $3\frac{2}{5}$ meters of ribbon for a project. How many meters of ribbon does Jenna have left?

_____

2. Brandon has a male puppy with a mass of $3\frac{1}{2}$ kilograms and a female puppy with a mass of $2\frac{1}{5}$ kilograms. How much greater is the male puppy's mass than the female puppy's?

_____

3. Jeff's sister drives 14 miles to her college, but his brother only drives $5\frac{7}{10}$ miles to his college. How much farther does Jeff's sister drive than his brother?

_____

4. Montel bought a spool of string for making kites. It contained $10\frac{3}{20}$ meters of string. He used $6\frac{9}{10}$ meters of string for kites. How many meters of string does Montel have left?

_____

5. Janet grew a pumpkin that weighs $13\frac{1}{2}$ pounds and a melon that weighs $8\frac{1}{4}$ pounds. How much heavier is the pumpkin than the melon?

_____

6. Aidan roller-skated $3\frac{1}{10}$ miles around the lake. Josh roller-skated $2\frac{1}{2}$ miles around the park. How much farther did Aidan roller-skate than Josh?

_____

1. Which of the fractions is equivalent to $\frac{1}{2}$?

   A $\frac{2}{6}$

   B $\frac{4}{8}$

   C $\frac{6}{10}$

   D $\frac{9}{12}$

2. Derek has 164 marbles. He gave 65 to his sister. How many marbles does he have left?

   A 89

   B 90

   C 99

   D 109

3. What is the mixed number for $\frac{8}{3}$?

   A $1\frac{2}{3}$

   B $2\frac{2}{3}$

   C $3\frac{2}{3}$

   D $4\frac{2}{3}$

4. Place these fractions in order from least to greatest. Explain how you decided.

   $\frac{1}{4}, \frac{1}{12}, \frac{1}{2}, \frac{1}{10}, \frac{1}{6}, \frac{1}{3}$

   _____

   _____

   _____

   _____

   _____

   _____

   _____

5. **Mental Math** John took $\frac{4}{5}$ of the marbles from a jar. What fraction of the marbles was left in the jar?

   _____

6. There are 4 computer labs at a school. Each computer lab holds 15 computers. How many computers are there in all?

   _____

   _____

Decomposing and Composing Fractions

Example 1

$\frac{1}{9}$
$+ \frac{2}{9}$

The denominators are the same, so you can add the numerators.

$\frac{3}{9} = \frac{1}{3}$ Rewrite $\frac{3}{9}$ as $\frac{1}{3}$

Example 2

$\frac{1}{8} + \frac{3}{8} + \frac{5}{8} = \frac{9}{8}$ or $1\frac{1}{8}$

Show another way to make this sum.

$\frac{6}{8} + \frac{3}{8} = \frac{9}{8} = 1\frac{1}{8}$

Add or subtract fractions and write answers in simplest form.
For the addition problems, write another addition problem that
has the same sum and uses two or more fractions.

1. $\frac{1}{4} + \frac{1}{4}$

2. $\frac{2}{3} - \frac{1}{3}$

3. $\frac{2}{8} + \frac{5}{8}$

4. $\frac{5}{6} - \frac{1}{6}$

5. $\frac{4}{12} + \frac{2}{12}$

_____   _____   _____   _____   _____

6. $\frac{5}{6}$
$- \frac{2}{6}$

7. $\frac{3}{10}$
$+ \frac{3}{10}$

8. $\frac{9}{10}$
$- \frac{3}{10}$

9. $\frac{3}{12}$
$+ \frac{6}{12}$

10. $\frac{44}{100}$
$- \frac{24}{100}$

11. At lunch, Alice ate $\frac{3}{8}$ of her sandwich. Later, for a snack, she ate another $\frac{3}{8}$ of the sandwich. Write an addition sentence that shows how much of the sandwich Alice ate. Suppose Alice ate the same total amount of her sandwich at 3 different times instead of 2. Write an addition problem that shows the amount she ate as a sum of 3 fractions.

_____

_____

R 12·10

Decomposing and Composing Fractions

For **1** through **15**, add or subtract the fractions. For the addition problems, write another addition problem that has the same sum and uses two or more fractions.

1. $\frac{1}{8} + \frac{3}{8} =$ _____

2. $\frac{8}{10} + \frac{1}{10} =$ _____

3. $\frac{1}{3} + \frac{1}{3} =$ _____

4. $\begin{array}{r} \frac{3}{8} \\ + \frac{3}{8} \\ \hline \end{array}$

5. $\begin{array}{r} \frac{1}{5} \\ + \frac{2}{5} \\ \hline \end{array}$

6. $\begin{array}{r} \frac{3}{6} \\ + \frac{2}{6} \\ \hline \end{array}$

7. $\frac{9}{12} - \frac{2}{12} =$ _____

8. $\frac{4}{8} - \frac{2}{8} =$ _____

9. $\frac{6}{10} - \frac{1}{10} =$ _____

10. $\begin{array}{r} \frac{5}{8} \\ - \frac{2}{8} \\ \hline \end{array}$

11. $\begin{array}{r} \frac{7}{10} \\ - \frac{1}{10} \\ \hline \end{array}$

12. $\begin{array}{r} \frac{8}{10} \\ - \frac{4}{10} \\ \hline \end{array}$

13. $\begin{array}{r} \frac{1}{6} \\ + \frac{2}{6} \\ \hline \end{array}$

14. $\begin{array}{r} \frac{1}{3} \\ + \frac{1}{3} \\ \hline \end{array}$

15. $\begin{array}{r} \frac{1}{4} \\ + \frac{1}{4} \\ \hline \end{array}$

16. Jacob is making a stew. The stew calls for $\frac{3}{8}$ cup of rice. If he triples the recipe, how much rice will he need? Write an addition problem to show your answer.

_____

17. Which of the following fractions is not an equivalent fraction to $\frac{1}{2}$?

A $\frac{3}{6}$ **B** $\frac{4}{8}$ **C** $\frac{6}{10}$ **D** $\frac{6}{12}$

18. **Writing to Explain** Gerry folded $\frac{3}{8}$ of the pile of shirts. Molly folded $\frac{1}{8}$ of the pile of shirts. Together, did they fold more than half the shirts? Explain your answer.

_____

_____

Boxes of Fractions

Complete each fraction box. Start with the fraction in the circle
and add or subtract the fraction in the inner box to get the fraction
in each outer corner.

Write your answers in simplest form.

One subtraction in Exercise 1 has been completed for you.

1.

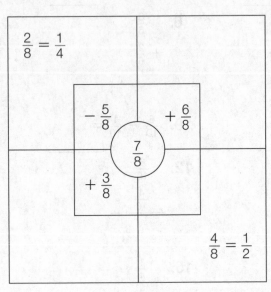

2.

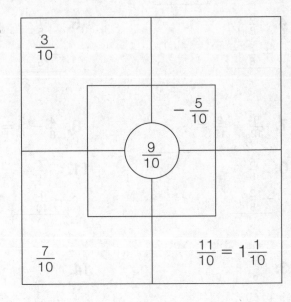

3.

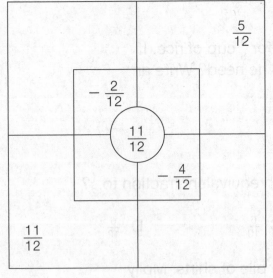

4.

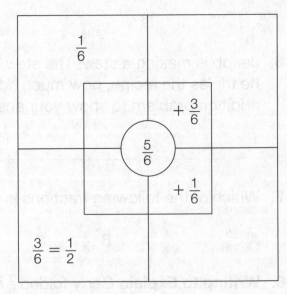

1. A deli is open 5 days a week for 5 hours each day. One week the deli served 925 customers. If the same number of customers were served each hour, how many were served each hour?

   A 185

   B 125

   C 37

   D 16

2. Giovanni had an orange with 12 sections. He gave 3 sections to Lucia and 4 sections to Ricky. What fraction of the orange did Giovanni have left?

   A $\frac{7}{12}$

   B $\frac{5}{12}$

   C $\frac{5}{7}$

   D $\frac{1}{4}$

3. Choose a fraction to make the inequality true.

   $\frac{3}{5} > \boxed{}$

   A $\frac{4}{5}$

   B $\frac{3}{6}$

   C $\frac{4}{6}$

   D $\frac{5}{6}$

4. **Estimation** Mr. Rosenthal is getting ready to build a dog house. He buys some wood for $33, some shingles for $12, and some screws for $7. About how much does he spend on the building materials?

   _____

5. What is the missing number in this equation? Explain how you know.

   $2 \times (10 \times 3) = (\boxed{} \times 10) \times 3$

   What property does the equation illustrate?

   _____

   _____

   _____

   _____

   _____

   _____

   _____

Problem Solving: Draw a Picture and Write an Equation

Read and Understand   Pippa filled $\frac{1}{8}$ of a jar with blue stones, $\frac{2}{8}$ of the jar with yellow stones, and $\frac{4}{8}$ of the jar with purple stones. How much of the jar is filled in all?

What do I know?   Pippa filled $\frac{1}{8}$, $\frac{2}{8}$, and $\frac{4}{8}$ of a jar.

What am I asked to find?   How much of the jar is filled with stones?

Plan   Draw a picture and write an equation.

$$\frac{1}{8} + \frac{2}{8} + \frac{4}{8} = x$$

Solve   Find equal fractions and add. Simplify if you need to.

$$\frac{1}{8} + \frac{2}{8} + \frac{4}{8} = \frac{7}{8}$$
$$x = \frac{7}{8}$$

Pippa filled the jar $\frac{7}{8}$ full of stones.

Draw a picture and write an equation to solve.

1. Joel walked $\frac{4}{12}$ of a mile to the store, $\frac{3}{12}$ of a mile to the library, and $\frac{2}{12}$ of a mile to the post office. Let x = the total distance Joel walked. How far did he walk?

_____

2. Midge walked $\frac{3}{4}$ mile Monday and $\frac{1}{4}$ mile Tuesday. Let x = how much farther she walked on Monday. How much farther did Midge walk on Monday?

_____

3. Number Sense Glenda wrote $\frac{2}{10}$ of her paper on Monday, $\frac{1}{10}$ of her paper on Tuesday, and $\frac{1}{10}$ of her paper on Wednesday. She said she wrote more than half of her paper. Is she correct? Why or why not?

_____

_____

Problem Solving: Draw a Picture and Write an Equation

Draw a picture and write an equation to solve.

1. Jamie bought $\frac{5}{8}$ pound of wheat flour. He also bought $\frac{2}{8}$ pound of white flour. How much flour did he buy?

2. Katie is $\frac{6}{10}$ of the way to Brianna's house. Larry is $\frac{7}{10}$ of the way to Brianna's house. How much closer to Brianna's house is Larry?

3. Nina practiced the trumpet for $\frac{1}{6}$ hour. Santiago practiced the trumpet for $\frac{4}{6}$ hour. How much longer did Santiago practice than Nina?

4. Ned caught $\frac{4}{12}$ pound of fish. Sarah caught $\frac{5}{12}$ pound of fish. Jessa caught $\frac{6}{12}$ pound of fish. Which bar diagram shows how to find how many pounds of fish they caught in all?

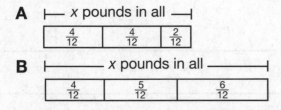

A ⊢— x pounds in all —⊣

| $\frac{4}{12}$ | $\frac{4}{12}$ | $\frac{2}{12}$ |

B ⊢———— x pounds in all ————⊣

| $\frac{4}{12}$ | $\frac{5}{12}$ | $\frac{6}{12}$ |

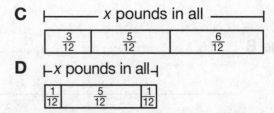

C ⊢———— x pounds in all ————⊣

| $\frac{3}{12}$ | $\frac{5}{12}$ | $\frac{6}{12}$ |

D ⊢x pounds in all⊣

| $\frac{1}{12}$ | $\frac{5}{12}$ | $\frac{1}{12}$ |

5. John had $\frac{5}{8}$ of a pizza left after a party. He gave $\frac{3}{8}$ of the pizza to his friend to take home and he kept the rest. Draw a picture showing what fraction of the pizza John kept, and write an equation to solve.

_____

_____

Crazy Quilt

The plan at the right is for a quilt
that the fifth grade is making.
Use the clues below to color or
label the different squares.

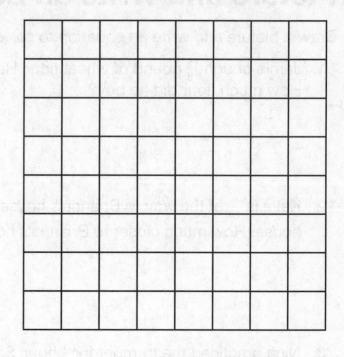

Clue A $\frac{1}{16}$ of the quilt is colored
yellow. It is in the center.

Clue B $\frac{28}{64}$ of the quilt is purple.
It does not touch the blue part.

Clue C $\frac{12}{64}$ of the quilt is blue.
It goes around the yellow section.

Clue D The green section of
the quilt takes up all the remaining
squares. Write a fraction that tells
about the green section.

_____

Create Your Own Plan a quilt using the grid on the right.
Keep it a secret! Write some clues using fractions and give
it to a classmate to solve.

Clue A _____

_____

Clue B _____

_____

Clue C _____

_____

Clue D _____

_____

Name _____

1. How would you write the number modeled below in standard form?

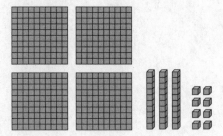

   A 348

   B 384

   C 438

   D 834

2. Which number completes the number sentence below?

$21 = \underline{\hspace{1cm}} + (6 + 8)$

   A 6

   B 7

   C 14

   D 35

3. Choose a fraction to make the sentence true.

$\frac{3}{5} > \square$

   A $\frac{4}{5}$

   B $\frac{3}{6}$

   C $\frac{4}{6}$

   D $\frac{5}{6}$

4. The table below shows the population of 4 cities.

City	Population
Happy Valley	49,604
Lakeside	50,104
Stoneyville	49,984
Rutherton	50,673

Write the numbers in order from greatest to least.

_____

_____

5. Hilda has 9 trading cards. Kevin has 14 more cards than Hilda. Tom has 3 fewer cards than Kevin. Write a number sentence to show how many cards Tom has.

_____

6. Which is longer, 5 feet or 2 feet?

_____

Name _____

Fractions as Multiples of Unit Fractions: Using Models

Ricardo has an apple that is cut into quarters.

He wants to eat $\frac{3}{4}$ of the apple.

How many $\frac{1}{4}$ pieces does he need to make $\frac{3}{4}$?

Use fraction strips and a number line.

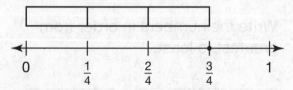

Each fraction strip equals $\frac{1}{4}$.

There are three $\frac{1}{4}$ fraction strips.

$$\frac{3}{4} = 3 \times \frac{1}{4}$$

Ricardo needs three $\frac{1}{4}$ pieces to make $\frac{3}{4}$.

In **1** and **2**, use the number line and fraction strips to complete the equation.

1.

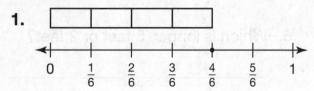

$\frac{4}{6} = $ _____ $\times$ _____

2.

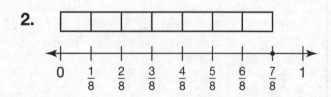

$\frac{7}{8} = $ _____ $\times$ _____

Fractions as Multiples of Unit Fractions: Using Models

For **1** through **9**, write the fraction as a multiple of a unit fraction.
Use fraction strips to help.

1. $\frac{2}{4}$ = _____

2. $\frac{4}{6}$ = _____

3. $\frac{3}{5}$ = _____

4. $\frac{3}{3}$ = _____

5. $\frac{7}{8}$ = _____

6. $\frac{6}{2}$ = _____

7. $\frac{5}{6}$ = _____

8. $\frac{9}{5}$ = _____

9. $\frac{8}{3}$ = _____

10. Use the picture at the right to write a
multiplication equation with $\frac{1}{2}$ as a factor.
Explain how you found the answer.

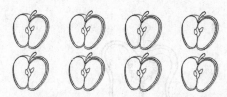

_____

_____

_____

11. How can you tell that a fraction is a unit fraction?

_____

_____

12. Which equation describes the picture?

A $\frac{1}{5} = 5 \times \frac{1}{2}$

B $\frac{1}{2} = 5 \times \frac{1}{2}$

C $\frac{5}{2} = 5 \times \frac{1}{5}$

D $\frac{5}{2} = 5 \times \frac{1}{2}$

Fraction Models

Look at the picture.
Write the numbers that make the multiplication equation true.

1.

2.

_____ = _____ × $\frac{1}{2}$ _____ = 2 × _____

3.

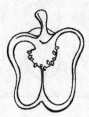

4.

_____ = _____ × $\frac{1}{2}$ _____ = _____ × $\frac{1}{4}$

5.

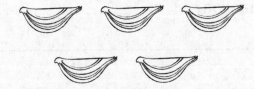

6.

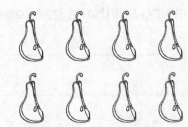

$\frac{5}{4}$ = _____ × _____   _____ = 8 × $\frac{1}{3}$

Name _____

1. How many hundreds are in 17,000?

   A 17,000

   B 1,700

   C 170

   D 17

2. Estimation Round 325,180 to the nearest ten thousand.

   A 330,000

   B 325,200

   C 325,000

   D 320,000

3. Notebooks cost $4. If Jade buys 3 notebooks, how much will they cost altogether?

   A $4

   B $7

   C $10

   D $12

4. Which number is greater than 38,246?

   A 37,236

   B 38,236

   C 38,240

   D 38,642

5. Which point on the number line represents 2,475?

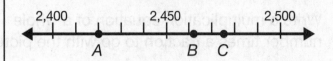

6. Mental Math Susan bought 8 packages of colored paper. Each package holds 100 sheets. How many sheets did Susan buy?

_____

7. Write three numbers that are greater than 67,000, but less than 68,000.

_____

_____

_____

8. Write the number 302,073 in word form.

_____

_____

Multiplying a Fraction by a Whole Number: Using Models

Write a multiplication equation of a whole number times a fraction to go with the picture.

$\frac{1}{5}$	$\frac{1}{5}$	$\frac{1}{5}$	$\frac{1}{5}$	$\frac{1}{5}$	$\frac{1}{5}$

Find the unit fraction: $\frac{1}{5}$

Count the number of unit fractions: 6

Write a multiplication equation to show the number of unit fractions times the unit fraction. $6 \times \frac{1}{5} = \blacksquare$

Multiply to find the product. $6 \times \frac{1}{5} = \frac{6}{5}$

The multiplication equation that goes with the picture is $6 \times \frac{1}{5} = \frac{6}{5}$.

In **1–2**, write a multiplication equation of a whole number and a fraction to go with the picture.

1.

$\frac{1}{3}$	$\frac{1}{3}$	$\frac{1}{3}$	$\frac{1}{3}$	$\frac{1}{3}$	$\frac{1}{3}$	$\frac{1}{3}$	$\frac{1}{3}$

Unit fraction: _____

Number of unit fractions: _____

Multiplication equation: _____

2.

$\frac{1}{4}$	$\frac{1}{4}$	$\frac{1}{4}$	$\frac{1}{4}$	$\frac{1}{4}$	$\frac{1}{4}$	$\frac{1}{4}$	$\frac{1}{4}$	$\frac{1}{4}$

Unit fraction: _____

Number of unit fractions: _____

Multiplication equation: _____

Multiplying a Fraction by a Whole Number: Using Models

For **1–3**, use each model to write a multiplication equation with a whole number and a fraction.

1.

| $\frac{1}{6}$ | $\frac{1}{6}$ | $\frac{1}{6}$ | $\frac{1}{6}$ | $\frac{1}{6}$ | $\frac{1}{6}$ | $\frac{1}{6}$ | $\frac{1}{6}$ | $\frac{1}{6}$ | $\frac{1}{6}$ |

$\underbrace{\qquad}_{\frac{5}{6}}$ $\underbrace{\qquad}_{\frac{5}{6}}$

_____

2.

| $\frac{4}{12}$ | $\frac{4}{12}$ | $\frac{4}{12}$ | $\frac{4}{12}$ | $\frac{4}{12}$ |

_____

3.

$\frac{3}{10}$ $\frac{3}{10}$ $\frac{3}{10}$

_____

4. Reason Write a multiplication equation of a whole number times a fraction to go with the number line.

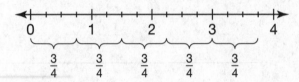

_____

5. Model Explain why $4 \times \frac{3}{5} = \frac{(4 \times 3)}{5} = \frac{12}{5}$. Draw a picture.

_____

_____

6. Audrey uses $\frac{5}{8}$ cup of fruit in each smoothie she makes. She makes 6 smoothies to share with her friends. How many cups of fruit does she use?

| $\frac{5}{8}$ | $\frac{5}{8}$ | $\frac{5}{8}$ | $\frac{5}{8}$ | $\frac{5}{8}$ | $\frac{5}{8}$ |

A $3\frac{3}{8}$ cups   **C** $3\frac{3}{4}$ cups

B $3\frac{1}{2}$ cups   **D** $6\frac{5}{8}$ cups

Name _____

Writing Fraction Equations

Sometimes, you can write more than one multiplication equation of a whole number times a fraction.

The model to the right shows $\frac{8}{6}$.

Possible equations: $8 \times \frac{1}{6} = \frac{8}{6} = 1\frac{2}{6} = 1\frac{1}{3}$

$4 \times \frac{2}{6} = \frac{8}{6} = 1\frac{1}{3}$

$2 \times \frac{4}{6} = \frac{8}{6} = 1\frac{1}{3}$

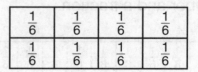

In **1–4**, write as many multiplication equations of a whole number times a fraction as you can to go with each model.

1.

$\frac{1}{5}$	$\frac{1}{5}$	$\frac{1}{5}$
$\frac{1}{5}$	$\frac{1}{5}$	$\frac{1}{5}$

_____

_____

2.

$\frac{1}{9}$	$\frac{1}{9}$	$\frac{1}{9}$	$\frac{1}{9}$	$\frac{1}{9}$
$\frac{1}{9}$	$\frac{1}{9}$	$\frac{1}{9}$	$\frac{1}{9}$	$\frac{1}{9}$
$\frac{1}{9}$	$\frac{1}{9}$	$\frac{1}{9}$	$\frac{1}{9}$	$\frac{1}{9}$
$\frac{1}{9}$	$\frac{1}{9}$	$\frac{1}{9}$	$\frac{1}{9}$	$\frac{1}{9}$

_____

_____

3.

$\frac{1}{4}$	$\frac{1}{4}$	$\frac{1}{4}$	$\frac{1}{4}$	$\frac{1}{4}$	$\frac{1}{4}$
$\frac{1}{4}$	$\frac{1}{4}$	$\frac{1}{4}$	$\frac{1}{4}$	$\frac{1}{4}$	$\frac{1}{4}$
$\frac{1}{4}$	$\frac{1}{4}$	$\frac{1}{4}$	$\frac{1}{4}$	$\frac{1}{4}$	$\frac{1}{4}$

_____

_____

4.

$\frac{1}{10}$	$\frac{1}{10}$	$\frac{1}{10}$
$\frac{1}{10}$	$\frac{1}{10}$	$\frac{1}{10}$
$\frac{1}{10}$	$\frac{1}{10}$	$\frac{1}{10}$
$\frac{1}{10}$	$\frac{1}{10}$	$\frac{1}{10}$

_____

_____

5. Generalize Explain how you were able to find all the possible multiplication equations of a whole number times a fraction to go with each picture.

_____

1. Yvette's computer has a folder with files shown by rows and columns. There are 4 rows and 12 columns. Which number sentence will tell you how many files the folder has?

   A $4 \times 12 = 48$

   B $12 - 4 = 8$

   C $4 + 12 = 16$

   D $12 \div 4 = 3$

2. Last year a bagel shop sold eighty-four thousand, seven hundred six bagels. Which shows this number?

   A 840,760

   B 840,706

   C 84,760

   D 84,706

3. Nick has 1,263 baseball cards. He gives 374 to his younger sister. How many baseball cards does Nick have now?

   A 889

   B 899

   C 989

   D 999

4. Which of the following numbers is less than 468,112?

   A 470,000

   B 469,000

   C 468,125

   D 468,100

5. What type of polygon has four sides of equal length and four right angles?

   _____

6. The table shows how many ounces of pebbles four friends have. Place the amounts in order from greatest to least.

Person	Amount (oz)
Sven	$\frac{1}{2}$
Rita	$\frac{3}{8}$
Wendy	$\frac{5}{8}$
Carlos	$\frac{2}{3}$

   _____

7. **Estimation** Nina has 763 pennies in a jar. Harold has 839 pennies in a jar. Round each amount to the nearest hundred.

   _____

   _____

8. Brad started with 132 marbles, bought 24 more, and then won 23. How many marbles does Brad now have?

   _____

Name _____

Multiplying a Fraction by a Whole Number: Using Symbols

Josh has 4 pieces of rope. Each piece of rope is $\frac{3}{4}$ yard long. How many yards of rope does Josh have?

You can think of each piece of rope as a separate group. The size of each group is $\frac{3}{4}$ yard.

$$\frac{3}{4} + \frac{3}{4} + \frac{3}{4} + \frac{3}{4}$$

Since all of the groups are the same size, you can use multiplication to find the total.

$$4 \times \frac{3}{4} = \frac{(4 \times 3)}{4} = \frac{12}{4} = 3$$

Think: The number of groups times the size of each group.

Josh has 3 yards of rope.

Solve. Show your work.

1. Mia is painting her room. Her room has 4 walls. Each wall uses $\frac{2}{3}$ gallon of paint. How much paint does she need to paint all of her walls?

$$\frac{2}{3} + \frac{2}{3} + \frac{2}{3} + \frac{2}{3} = 4 \times \frac{2}{3}$$

$$4 \times \frac{2}{3} = \rule{5cm}{0.4pt}$$

2. Nat has 5 pieces of string. Each piece is $\frac{7}{8}$ inch long. How many inches of string does Nat have?

$$\frac{7}{8} + \frac{7}{8} + \frac{7}{8} + \frac{7}{8} + \frac{7}{8} = 5 \times \frac{7}{8}$$

$$5 \times \frac{7}{8} = \rule{5cm}{0.4pt}$$

3. Caroline is making 8 batches of biscuits. Each batch uses $\frac{5}{6}$ cup of flour. How many cups of flour does Caroline need?

_____

_____

Multiplying a Fraction by a Whole Number: Using Symbols

For **1–8**, multiply.

1. $8 \times \frac{5}{12} =$ _____

2. $9 \times \frac{1}{4} =$ _____

3. $5 \times \frac{3}{5} =$ _____

4. $10 \times \frac{5}{6} =$ _____

5. $9 \times \frac{3}{10} =$ _____

6. $7 \times \frac{1}{3} =$ _____

7. $12 \times \frac{1}{5} =$ _____

8. $11 \times \frac{7}{8} =$ _____

9. Model Matt is raking leaves for his neighbors. It takes him $\frac{7}{8}$ hour to rake the leaves in one lawn. How long will it take Matt to rake the leaves for 6 neighbors? Write a multiplication sentence to solve.

_____

10. Zoey is making bracelets for her friends. Each bracelet takes $\frac{5}{6}$ foot of string. How much string will Zoey need to make 12 bracelets?

_____

11. Farid takes $\frac{7}{8}$ teaspoon of allergy medicine every day. How much medicine will he take in one week?

A $1\frac{3}{4}$ teaspoons **B** $5\frac{1}{4}$ teaspoons **C** $6\frac{1}{8}$ teaspoons **D** $7\frac{7}{8}$ teaspoons

12. Writing to Explain Mrs. Nunez is correcting math tests. She corrects 7 tests before school, and 5 tests after school. If each test takes her $\frac{1}{5}$ hour to correct, how long will it take Mrs. Nunez to correct the tests? Explain.

_____

_____

_____

Turtle Race

The students in Mr. Stevens' class are having a turtle race. The race will last 2 minutes. Find the distance from the start each turtle will be at the end of the race.

Turtle	Speed (in inches per second)	Distance at end of race
Spot	$\frac{1}{6}$	
Rex	$\frac{2}{3}$	
Tim	$\frac{3}{5}$	
Milo	$\frac{1}{4}$	
Watson	$\frac{1}{8}$	
Tiny	$\frac{1}{2}$	
Bruno	$\frac{1}{3}$	
Squiggles	$\frac{3}{7}$	
Petey	$\frac{4}{9}$	
Lou	$\frac{2}{9}$	
Nate	$\frac{1}{7}$	
Troy	$\frac{2}{5}$	

1. What is the order of the turtles at the end of the race? Start with the winner.

_____

_____

2. If the winner had stayed still for the first half-minute of the race, how far would it have been from the start at the end of the race?

_____

3. What place would it have been in?

_____

1. Daryl is 23 years old. His brother Larry is 11 years younger. Which number sentence can you use to find how old Larry is?

   A $23 - 11 = 12$

   B $23 + 11 = 34$

   C $34 - 23 = 11$

   D $23 - 12 = 11$

2. Samantha ate $\frac{3}{8}$ of a pizza for lunch. Todd ate $\frac{1}{8}$ of the pizza. Which part of the pizza did they eat altogether?

   A All

   B $\frac{1}{2}$

   C $\frac{2}{3}$

   D $\frac{7}{8}$

3. Donna has read 9 times as many pages as Bob. Bob has read 8 pages. How many pages has Donna read?

   A 17

   B 54

   C 72

   D 81

4. Marissa has 79 grams of grapes. Roger has 81 grams of grapes. Whose grapes have a greater mass?

   _____

5. Dennis has 171 shells in his collection. Fred has 208. Round each amount to the nearest ten. About how many more shells does Fred have?

   _____

6. **Mental Math** Ian multiplied a number by 5. He then multiplied that product by 2. What digit is in the ones place of the final product?

   _____

Fractions and Decimals

Any fraction that has a denominator of 10 or 100 can be written as a decimal. Tenths and hundredths are written as digits to the right of the decimal point.

The shaded part is $\frac{2}{10}$ of the whole area.

Write it as a decimal: 0.2

Say: two tenths.

The shaded part is $\frac{13}{100}$ of the whole area.

Write it as a decimal: 0.13

Say: thirteen hundredths

Write a fraction and a decimal to tell how much is shaded.

1.

2.

3. How are the two shaded grids alike? How are they different?

_____

_____

_____

_____

_____

_____   _____

Write each fraction as a decimal.

4. $\frac{3}{10}$ **5.** $\frac{9}{10}$ **6.** $\frac{9}{100}$ **7.** $\frac{27}{100}$

_____   _____   _____   _____

Write each decimal as a fraction in its simplest form.

8. 0.40   **9.** 0.76   **10.** 4.8   **11.** 0.07

_____   _____   _____   _____

Fractions and Decimals

Write a fraction and a decimal to show how much is shaded.

1.

_____

2.

_____

3.
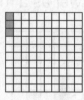
_____

Draw a model that shows each decimal.

4. 0.16

5. 1.7

6. 0.78

Write each fraction as a decimal.

7. $\frac{1}{100}$

8. $9\frac{4}{10}$

9. $\frac{6}{10}$

10. $\frac{17}{100}$

_____

_____

_____

_____

Write each decimal as a fraction in its simplest form.

11. 0.5

12. 0.70

13. 0.3

14. 3.60

_____

_____

_____

_____

15. In the decimal models, how many strips equal 10 small squares?

A 70 strips

B 10 strips

C 7 strips

D 1 strip

16. Writing to Explain Explain the steps you would take to write $\frac{36}{10}$ as a decimal.

_____

_____

_____

Shady Spots

Each grid stands for one dollar. Darcy shaded designs to show
parts of a dollar. How much of each large square is shaded?
Write your answer as a money amount, a decimal, and a fraction.

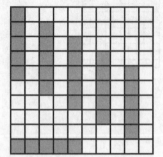

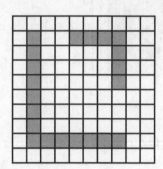

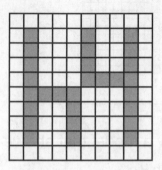

1. _____

2. _____

3. _____

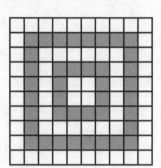

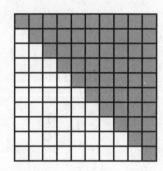

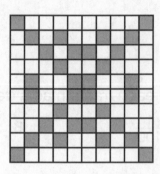

4. _____

5. _____

6. _____

Shade a design to show the money amount.

7. $0.20

8. $0.46

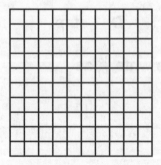

Name _____

1. A park baseball league had 54 people sign up to play. Each team will have 9 players. Which number sentence is in the same fact family as $54 \div 9 = \square$?

   A $4 \times 9 = \square$

   B $45 \div \square = 9$

   C $\square \times 6 = 54$

   D $54 \times 9 = \square$

2. **Mental Math** The two pie pans below show what was left of two pies.

   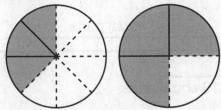

   Which of the following compares the portions of pie left in each pan?

   A $\frac{3}{8} > \frac{3}{4}$

   B $\frac{3}{8} < \frac{3}{4}$

   C $\frac{3}{4} < \frac{3}{8}$

   D $\frac{3}{4} = \frac{3}{8}$

3. In which number sentence does 7 make the equation true?

   A $\square \div 5 = 2$

   B $36 \div 6 = \square$

   C $56 \div \square = 8$

   D $\square \div 4 = 3$

4. On the last day of school, Samantha's class released 112 balloons into the sky. Thirty-six balloons popped in just a few seconds. How many balloons were left?

   _____

5. Ryan has four pets named Brandy, Bailey, Jimmy, and Sparky. One is a cat, one is a fish, one is a bird, and one is a dog. Brandy is a dog. Bailey is not a bird. Sparky is a fish. What kind of animal is Jimmy? Write the answer in a complete sentence.

   _____

6. A small watch company sells about 35 watches each day. About how many watches does the company sell in one week if it is open every day?

   _____

Fractions and Decimals on the Number Line

How do you locate fractions and decimals on a number line?

Show $\frac{1}{8}$ on a number line.

Draw a number line and label 0 and 1. Divide the distance from 0 to 1 into 8 equal lengths.

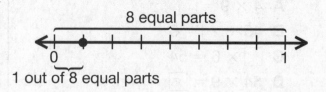

8 equal parts

1 out of 8 equal parts

Label 0, $\frac{1}{8}$, $\frac{2}{8}$, $\frac{3}{8}$, $\frac{4}{8}$, $\frac{5}{8}$, $\frac{6}{8}$, $\frac{7}{8}$, and 1.

Draw a point at $\frac{1}{8}$.

Show 0.3 on another number line.

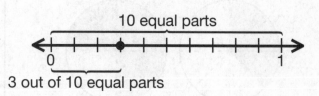

10 equal parts

3 out of 10 equal parts

Draw another number line and label 0 and 1. Divide the distance from 0 to 1 into 10 equal lengths.

Label 0.1, 0.2, 0.3, 0.4, and so on.

Use the number line to name the fraction that should be written at each point.

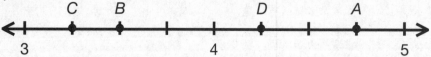

1. A _____   **2.** B _____   **3.** C _____   **4.** D _____

Identify the correct point on the number line for each fraction or decimal.

5. $6\frac{1}{3}$ _____   **6.** 5.3 _____   **7.** $5\frac{2}{3}$ _____   **8.** 6.8 _____

Fractions and Decimals on the Number Line

Use the number line to name the fraction or decimal that should be written at each point.

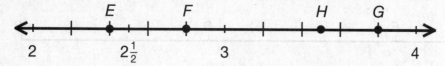

1. E _____ 2. F _____ 3. G _____ 4. H _____

Identify the correct point on the number line for each fraction or decimal.

5. 8.3 _____ 6. $7\frac{3}{5}$ _____ 7. 7.7 _____ 8. 8.2 _____

9. Eamon used a number line to compare two numbers, 0.48 and $\frac{3}{5}$. One number was less than $\frac{1}{2}$ and the other number was greater than $\frac{1}{2}$. Which number was less than $\frac{1}{2}$? _____

10. **Writing to Explain** Jayne says that 0.45 is equal to $\frac{4}{10}$. Is she correct? Explain.

_____

_____

_____

A New Measure

Distance $\overline{AB}$ is a new measurement called a pflugel.

```
A                              C                    B
|_____|

A                        F              D            B
|_____|

A       E       G       H       C                    B
|_____|
```

Write the fractional part of a pflugel.

1. Distance $\overline{DB}$ _____

2. Distance $\overline{AE}$ _____

3. Distance $\overline{EC}$ _____

4. Distance $\overline{GB}$ _____

Write the decimal part of a pflugel.

5. Distance $\overline{AG}$ _____

6. Distance $\overline{CB}$ _____

7. Distance $\overline{CG}$ _____

8. Distance $\overline{AC}$ _____

Name _____

1. **Estimation** The rain gauge at the airport recorded that it rained 127 inches in one year. What is this amount rounded to the nearest ten?

   A 100 inches

   B 110 inches

   C 120 inches

   D 130 inches

2. Kate writes two equivalent fractions for the shaded part of the rectangle.

   What two fractions could Kate write?

   A $\frac{2}{6}$ and $\frac{4}{12}$

   B $\frac{2}{8}$ and $\frac{1}{4}$

   C $\frac{2}{8}$ and $\frac{4}{8}$

   D $\frac{6}{8}$ and $\frac{2}{8}$

3. Which shows the factors of 10?

   A 1, 2, 5, 10

   B 10, 20, 30, 40

   C 2, 5

   D 1, 2, 3, 5, 6, 10

4. Zada says that 9, 15, and 24 are multiples of a number. What is the number?

   _____

5. Mateo measured the length of an insect. He found it was between $3\frac{1}{5}$ and $3\frac{3}{10}$ inches long. Write a mixed number that could be the length of the insect. Explain how you found your answer.

   _____

   _____

   _____

Equivalent Fractions and Decimals

A fraction and a decimal can both be used to represent the same value.

Write $\frac{6}{12}$ as a decimal.

Step 1 Write the fraction in simplest form.

$$\frac{6}{12} = \frac{1}{2}$$

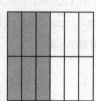

Step 2 Rename the fraction using a denominator of 10, 100, or 1,000.

Think: What number times 2 equals 10?

$$\frac{1}{2} = \frac{5}{10}$$

Step 3 Write the decimal.

$\frac{5}{10}$ is five tenths.

$$\frac{5}{10} = 0.5$$

So, $\frac{6}{12} = 0.5$

In **1** through **4**, find the missing numbers. Then write each fraction as a decimal.

1. $\frac{1}{4} = \frac{\square}{100}$

2. $\frac{9}{20} = \frac{\square}{100}$

3. $\frac{3}{15} = \frac{1}{\square} = \frac{\square}{10}$

4. $\frac{8}{25} = \frac{\square}{100}$

_____   _____   _____   _____

Write each fraction as a decimal.

5. $\frac{4}{5}$

6. $\frac{4}{50}$

7. $\frac{4}{25}$

8. $\frac{13}{20}$

9. $\frac{9}{50}$

_____   _____   _____   _____   _____

Tell whether each pair shows equivalent numbers.

10. $\frac{2}{5}$; 0.25

11. $\frac{10}{25}$; 0.4

12. $\frac{3}{5}$; 0.35

13. $\frac{7}{20}$; 0.35

_____   _____   _____   _____

14. Nine out of 15, or $\frac{9}{15}$, of the people at the skating rink brought their own skates. Write an equivalent decimal for $\frac{9}{15}$. _____

Equivalent Fractions and Decimals

In **1** through **5**, write each fraction as a decimal.

1. $\frac{1}{5}$ **2.** $\frac{9}{12}$ **3.** $\frac{11}{25}$ **4.** $\frac{19}{20}$ **5.** $\frac{23}{50}$

_____   _____   _____   _____   _____

In **6** through **9**, tell whether each pair shows equivalent numbers.

6. $\frac{2}{5}$; 0.5   **7.** $\frac{7}{20}$; 0.07   **8.** $\frac{4}{16}$; 0.25   **9.** $\frac{11}{50}$; 0.22

_____   _____   _____   _____

10. A rock band has 5 members, and $\frac{2}{5}$ of the members play string instruments. Also, 0.4 of the members sing. Does the band have the same number of string instrument players as singers? Explain.

_____

11. Kevin has 20 words to learn for his spelling test on Friday. He has learned 6 of the words. So, he has learned $\frac{6}{20}$ of the words. Write $\frac{6}{20}$ in simplest form, and find an equivalent decimal.

_____

12. Which decimal is equivalent to $\frac{5}{20}$?

  A 0.20   **C** 0.35

  B 0.25   **D** 0.52

13. Gina wrote that $\frac{4}{5}$ is greater than 0.75. Is Gina correct? Explain why or why not.

_____

14. Look at Exercise 8. Explain how you decided whether the numbers are equivalent.

_____

_____

_____

Visualize Fractions and Decimals

Write a fraction in simplest form and a decimal for the shaded part of each shape.

1.

_____

2.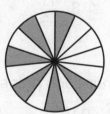

_____

3.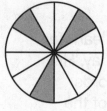

_____

4.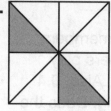

_____

5.

6.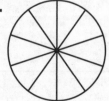

_____

Shade some parts of each shape below. Write a fraction in simplest form and a decimal to represent the shaded part of the shape.

7.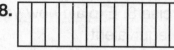

8.

1. Which digit is in the hundreds place in the number 34,863?

   A 8

   B 6

   C 4

   D 3

2. **Mental Math** Which is equal to 2 quarters and 9 dimes?

   A 4 quarters and 3 dimes

   B 14 dimes

   C 4 quarters and 5 dimes

   D 15 dimes

3. Which line on the figure divides the figure into two equal parts?

   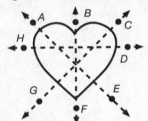

   A $\overleftrightarrow{AE}$

   B $\overleftrightarrow{BF}$

   C $\overleftrightarrow{CG}$

   D $\overleftrightarrow{DH}$

4. The table below shows the cost of a CD if you buy a certain number at Music To Go.

Cost of CDs				
Number of CDs	1–5	6–10	11–15	16–20
Cost per CD	$18	$15	?	$9

   Use the pattern in the table to find the cost per CD if you buy 12 CDs.

   _____

5. Adrian measured the thickness of a board and marked it as *A* on the number line below.

   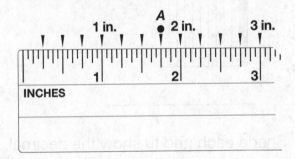

   How thick is the board?

   _____

6. Write 8,829 in expanded form.

   _____

Decimal Place Value

A grid can be used to show tenths and
hundredths. To show 0.3, you would shade 3
out of the 10 parts.

0.3
3 out of 10
parts are
shaded.

To show 0.30, you would shade 30 out of
the 100 parts.

0.30
30 out of 100
parts are
shaded.

One part of the hundredths grid can be
compared to a penny, since one part of the
grid is equal to 0.01 and a penny is equal to
one hundredth of a dollar.

Tenths and hundredths are related. In the above examples,
3 tenths or 30 hundredths of the grids are shaded, or 0.3 and
0.30. These numbers are equal: 0.3 = 0.30.

Write the word form and decimal for each shaded part.

1.

_____

2.

_____

Shade each grid to show the decimal.

3. 0.57

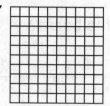

4. 0.4

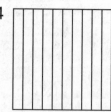

5. Number Sense Which is greater, 0.04 or 0.4? Explain.

_____

_____

_____

Name _____

Decimal Place Value

Write the word form and decimal for each shaded part.

1.

_____

2.

_____

For each fact, shade a grid to show the part of the population of each country that lives in cities.

3. In Jamaica, 0.5 of the people live in cities.

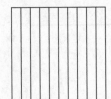

4. Only 0.11 of the population of Uganda live in cities.

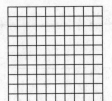

5. In Norway, 0.72 of the people live in cities.

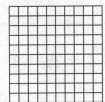

6. Which grid shows fourteen hundredths?

A   **B**   **C**   **D**

7. Writing to Explain Explain why one column in a hundredths grid is equal to one column in a tenths grid.

_____

_____

_____

Decimal Patterns

Write the next two numbers in each pattern.

1. 0.2, 0.4, 0.6, _____, _____

2. thirty-three hundredths, thirty-four hundredths, thirty-five hundredths,

   _____, _____

3. 1.7, 1.8, 1.9, _____, _____

4. fourteen hundredths, sixteen hundredths, eighteen hundredths,

   _____, _____

5. 1.27, 1.24, 1.21, 1.18, 1.15, _____, _____

6. two tenths, twenty hundredths, three tenths, thirty hundredths, four tenths,

   _____, _____

7. 1.45, 1.4, 1.35, 1.3, 1.25, _____, _____

8. three tenths, six tenths, nine tenths, one and two tenths, one and five tenths,

   _____, _____

9. five tenths, forty-five hundredths, four tenths, thirty-five hundredths, three tenths,

   _____, _____

10. 2.2, 2.0, 1.8, 1.6, 1.4, _____, _____

11. 0.09, 0.14, 0.19, 0.24, 0.29, _____, _____

12. thirty-seven hundredths, thirty-three hundredths, twenty-nine hundredths, twenty-five hundredths, twenty-one hundredths,

   _____, _____

1. Darlene measures the mass of a small rock in science class and finds it is 6.15 grams. How would she say this number in word form?

   A Six hundred and fifteen hundredths

   B Six and fifteen tenths

   C Six and five tenths

   D Six and fifteen hundredths

2. Terrell bought 12 apples at the fruit stand. He gave some to his friends and had 7 left. How many apples did Terrell give away?

   A 5

   B 7

   C 12

   D 19

3. A bakery uses the baking pans shown below to make loaves of bread. Which two pans are the same size and the same shape?

   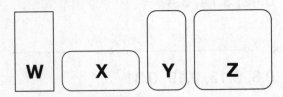

   A Pan W and pan X

   B Pan W and pan Y

   C Pan W and pan Z

   D Pan X and pan Y

4. **Estimation** The Art Museum had 355,288 visitors last year. The Science Museum had 305,965 visitors. Which museum had closer to 350,000 visitors?

   _____

5. Erika strings a necklace with 5 blue beads, 2 green beads, 4 purple beads, and then repeats the pattern. If she uses 10 blue beads, how many beads does she use altogether?

   _____

Comparing and Ordering Decimals

Compare 0.87 to 0.89.

First, begin at the left. Find the first place where the numbers are different.

0.87

0.89

The numbers are the same in the tenths place, so look to the next place.

The first place where the numbers are different is the hundredths place. Compare 7 hundredths to 9 hundredths.

0.07 < 0.09, so 0.87 < 0.89

Compare. Write >, <, or = for each ◯.

1. 0.36 ◯ 0.76

2. 5.1 ◯ 5.01

3. 1.2 ◯ 1.20

4. 6.55 ◯ 6.6

5. 0.62 ◯ 0.82

6. 4.71 ◯ 4.17

Order the numbers from least to greatest.

7. 1.36, 1.3, 1.63

8. 0.42, 3.74, 3.47

_____

_____

9. 6.46, 6.41, 4.6

10. 0.3, 0.13, 0.19, 0.31

_____

_____

11. Number Sense Which is greater, 8.0 or 0.8? Explain.

_____

_____

_____

Comparing and Ordering Decimals

Compare. Write >, <, or = for each ◯.

1. 0.31 ◯ 0.41   **2.** 1.9 ◯ 0.95   **3.** 0.09 ◯ 0.1

4. 2.70 ◯ 2.7   **5.** 0.81 ◯ 0.79   **6.** 2.12 ◯ 2.21

Order the numbers from least to greatest.

7. 0.37, 0.41, 0.31   **8.** 1.16, 1.61, 6.11

_____   _____

9. 7.9, 7.91, 7.09, 7.19   **10.** 1.45, 1.76, 1.47, 1.67

_____   _____

Margaret has three cats. Sophie weighs 4.27 lb, Tigger weighs
6.25 lb, and Ghost weighs 4.7 lb.

11. Which cat has the greatest weight?   _____

12. Which cat weighs the least?   _____

13. Which group of numbers is ordered from least to greatest?

    A 0.12, 1.51, 0.65

    B 5.71, 5.4, 0.54

    C 0.4, 0.09, 0.41

    D 0.05, 0.51, 1.5

14. **Writing to Explain** Darrin put the numbers 7.25, 7.52, 5.72,
and 5.27 in order from greatest to least. Is his work correct?
Explain.

_____

_____

Do We Decimal?

In many libraries, nonfiction books are placed on shelves in order according to the Dewey Decimal System.

Help the librarian decide where to put the list of books that have been returned. Write the abbreviation for the section where each returned book should be placed. Then write the exact place where each book should be shelved. The first book has been done for you.

003.1	027.4	029.9	038.1	042.1	042.9	047.01	051.1	056.12	057.1	057.19	058.7

General (G)

102.2	107.31	116.09	122.05	122.96	147.3	151.61	151.9	152.09	153.6

Philosophy & Psychology (PP)

510.10	516.05	521.3	550.11	551.62	563.07	572.1	574.73	581.71	586.8	587.09	587.22	591.6

Sciences & Mathematics (SM)

808.1	812.4	813.21	856.65	881.9	882.4	886.89

Literature (L)

1. 109.7   PP; Between 107.31 and 116.09

2. 152.08 _____

3. 042.13 _____

4. 006.8 _____

5. 503.54 _____

6. 550.06 _____

7. 813.12 _____

8. 107.05 _____

9. 886.9 _____

10. 057.01 _____

11. 587.21 _____

12. 122.5 _____

Name _____

1. In the picture below, each square of the grid represents 1 square foot.

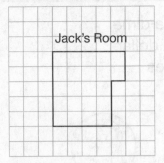

Jack's Room

What is the area of Jack's room?

A 10 square feet

B 17 square feet

C 22 square feet

D 25 square feet

2. **Estimation** Last year, 288 people saw the school play. This year, 965 people saw the play. Which is the best estimate of how many more people saw the play this year?

A 300 more people

B 600 more people

C 700 more people

D 1,000 more people

3. You buy a sandwich and receive $4.09 in change. How many coins do you have if you were given the fewest coins possible?

A 4 coins

B 5 coins

C 7 coins

D 9 coins

4. Which place value would you use to show that 4,532 is less than 4,541?

_____

5. The table below shows the numbers of magazines sold by four schools in a fundraiser contest.

School	Magazines Sold	Prize
Jefferson School	1,569	First
Adams School	1,532	
Harding School	1,505	
Hammond School	1,560	

Order the numbers to find which schools came in second place, third place, and fourth place.

_____

_____

_____

Name _____

Using Money to Understand Decimals

We can use money to understand decimals. For example, a dime is one-tenth of a dollar, or 0.1. It takes 10 dimes to equal a dollar. A penny is one one-hundredth of a dollar, or 0.01, so it takes 100 pennies to equal one dollar.

| $0.01 | $0.05 | $0.10 | $0.25 | $0.50 |
| 0.01 | 0.05 | 0.1 | 0.25 | 0.5 |

The decimal point is read by saying "and." So, $1.99 is read as "one dollar *and* ninety-nine cents."

---

1. $3.52 = _____ dollars + _____ dimes + _____ pennies

2. $1.87 = _____ dollar + _____ dimes + _____ pennies

3. **Number Sense** Write nine and thirty-six hundredths with a decimal point.

_____

How could you use only dollars, dimes, and pennies to buy

4. the baseball?

_____

_____

5. the baseball bat?

_____

_____

$3.99

$8.49

$12.20

Using Money to Understand Decimals

1. 2.18 = _____ ones + _____ tenth + _____ hundredths

$2.18 = _____ dollars + _____ dime + _____ pennies

2. 9.27 = _____ ones + _____ hundredths

$9.27 = _____ dollars + _____ pennies

3. 7.39 = _____ ones + _____ tenths + _____ hundredths

$7.39 = _____ dollars + _____ dimes + _____ pennies

4. Number Sense Write 3 dollars, 9 dimes, and 5 pennies with a dollar sign and decimal point.

_____

5. Number Sense If you have 5 tenths of a dollar, how much money do you have?

_____

6. Lana wants to buy a book for $6.95. How can she pay for the book using only dollars, dimes, and nickels?

_____

7. How would you write sixteen and twenty-five hundredths with a decimal point?

A 16.025　　　**B** 16.25　　　**C** 162.5　　　**D** 1,625

8. Writing to Explain Which is greater, 4 tenths and 2 hundredths or 2 tenths and 4 hundredths? Explain.

_____

_____

_____

Name _____

Similar Shapes

Look at the group of shapes on the left and find something that
all of the shapes in the group have in common. Then, circle the
shape on the right that belongs in the group.

1.

 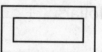

2.

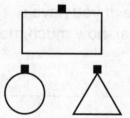

3.

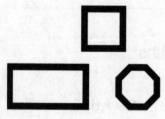

4.

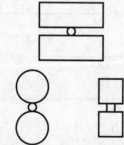

1. Mr. Thomas divided his class of 35 students into groups to play a game. There were 5 students in each group. Which number sentence is in the same fact family as $35 \div \square = 5$?

   A $5 \times 35 = \square$

   B $\square \times 7 = 35$

   C $70 \div \square = 7$

   D $5 \div 5 = \square$

2. **Estimation** Jayda is measuring an object's weight in pounds. Which of the following objects is she most likely measuring?

   A Shoebox

   B Dresser

   C Poster

   D Tennis ball

3. Carol has 4 bags of oranges. Laverne has more bags than Carol. Which expression represents how many bags Laverne has?

   A $4 \times x$

   B $4 \div x$

   C $4 + x$

   D $4 - x$

4. Monica has tiles that are 1 inch by 1 inch squares. If she uses them to make a rectangle that is 16 inches long and 6 inches wide, how many tiles will she use?

   _____

5. Darryl and 4 friends share 15 apples. What is the fair share for each of them?

   _____

6. Greta places carnations in $\frac{3}{8}$ of her pots and daisies in $\frac{1}{2}$ of her pots. Are there more pots with carnations or daisies?

   _____

Problem Solving:
Draw a Picture

A fence is 20 ft long. It has posts at each end and at every 4 ft along its length. How many fence posts are there?

Read and Understand

Step 1: What do you know?

The fence is 20 ft long.

There are fence posts at each end.

There are fence posts every 4 ft along the length of the fence.

Step 2: What are you trying to find?

How many posts the fence has.

Plan and Solve

Step 3: What strategy will you use?

Strategy: Draw a picture

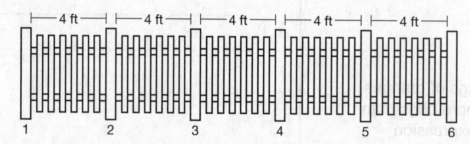

There are 6 fence posts altogether.

Look Back and Check

Step 4: Is your work correct?

Yes, the picture shows that there is a total of 6 fence posts.

Solve the problem. Write the answer in a complete sentence.

1. Tim, Kara, and Ann are working together to write a 4-page report. Each student is going to do an equal amount of writing. What fraction of the entire report does each student need to write?

Problem Solving:
Draw a Picture

Solve each problem. Write the answer in a complete sentence.

1. Three friends divided a veggie pizza into 12 slices. If they divide the pizza equally, what fraction of the pizza would each friend get?

_____

2. Mark is making a quilt with his grandmother. Each row of the quilt has 6 squares. There are 8 rows. $\frac{1}{2}$ of the squares are blue. How many blue squares are in the quilt?

_____

3. Jane pulled weeds in the garden 7 times. She was paid $5 each time she pulled weeds for less than 1 hour and $6 each time she pulled weeds for more than 1 hour. If Jane received $39, how many times did she pull weeds for more than 1 hour?

_____

_____

4. Neil needs to cut 3 long boards into 9 smaller boards. The first is 10 ft, the second is 16 ft, and the third is 18 ft. The table lists the smaller boards Neil needs. Use a drawing to show how he can divide the 3 boards so there is no waste.

Length of Board	Number Needed
4 ft	3
5 ft	4
6 ft	2

10 ft

16 ft

18 ft

Picture Patterns

Use the pictures to find the pattern. Then complete the table.

1.

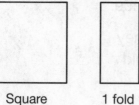

| Square piece of paper | 1 fold | 2 folds | 3 folds | 4 folds | 5 folds |

Number of folds	1	2	3	4	5
Number of parts	2	4	8		
Fraction for one part	$\frac{1}{2}$	$\frac{1}{4}$	$\frac{1}{8}$		

2.

Carton stack	A	B	C	D	E
Number of cartons	1	3			
Fraction for one carton	1	$\frac{1}{3}$			

3.

Figure	A	B	C	D	E
Number of squares	2				
Fraction of shaded squares	$\frac{1}{2}$				